REVEL

GEOL___.

A Believing Geoscientist's Investigation
of Prophesied Catastrophe & Rescue

By

Ryan Thompson

Leviathan Publishing
Sussex, England | Ooltewah, Tennessee

www.RemnantRendezvous.org

Book cover art by Shaun Moreland.

All Bible references are taken from the NKJV® unless noted as from the NASB®. The name of Jesus in these references has been replaced with Yeshua to more accurately transliterate his original Hebrew name. The text has also been replaced with YHWH where the tetragrammaton (the four Hebrew letters for the name of the Creator) appears in the original Hebrew.

Library of Congress Control Number: 2024900959
ISBN: 978-1-7384984-4-4 (Paperback)
ISBN: 978-1-7384984-9-9 (eBook)

Table of Contents

To the Creator:

For YHWH gives wisdom, from His mouth come knowledge and understanding. Proverbs 2:6

In the name of the Creator, the Most Merciful, the Especially Merciful...

Introduction

Geology, the study of the earth, is a science that most have only briefly encountered; touching on such popular subjects as dinosaurs or volcanos. It is often portrayed as a study of the distant past, and so is usually dismissed as irrelevant to modern life—but that is about to change. The majority are taught to believe that dinosaurs and other fossilized creatures lived many millions of years ago, and that they died and their bones were buried in sediment that slowly hardened into stone. Supposedly, this process of burying ancient life by gradually accumulating layers of sediment has remained uniform during the many intervening millions of years. However, there are a few scientists who question the assumptions needed to support this proposition. They have spent whole careers researching, and then showing how a vast amount of data may be interpreted to match the historical records of a global flood that occurred only a few thousand years ago and caused the creation of the entire fossil record. Regardless of what one chooses to believe, whether a few thousand years or a few hundred million years, geology is often thought of as a study of the past; but it does not have to be.

When studying geology, the most important principle applied is that present processes may be used to better understand what has happened in the past. Because major geologic catastrophes have not been common occurrences, those who teach that slow and steady processes prove that millions of years are required thus ignore major catastrophes altogether. As major events become increasingly numerous and more severe, such overly-simplistic reasoning will be replaced by the understanding that geologic processes occur very quickly due to severe catastrophic events.

The explosive eruption of Mount Saint Helens in May of 1980 is one such example which caused some to abandon the assumptions of slow, steady processes resulting in gradual geologic change over millions of years. Just this one single event brought about a renaissance in research projects where data was collected that supports the historical records of a global flood. Some of the scientists who performed this research also taught me how to ask challenging questions, make a few reasonable assumptions, and arrive at scientifically defensible conclusions. Their encouragement to believe in the scriptures is vital, and yet their version of geology is primarily focused on interpreting the past by using present events for guidance.

A major earthquake in south-central Turkey in February of 2023, and indeed the increasing number and severity of earthquakes around the world, are raising questions of what is coming next. The extent of devastation in that single earthquake could be described as apocalyptic, and yet the prophecies in scripture contain vivid warnings of future events far more catastrophic than any that have yet been witnessed. These warnings of danger contain many allusions to geologic events and processes presently witnessed on earth, just on a much more terrifying scale. If subtle geologic clues in scripture might be properly understood—if present geologic processes may also guide understanding the recorded future— then maybe some of the danger may be avoided.

Many skeptics will certainly deride the idea of combining scriptures and science in investigating the future. Most do not see how scriptures and science work together; the one from the mouth of the Creator and the other from His hand. They prefer to imagine life without a Creator to whom His creation would be responsible. They desire to live on their own terms, free from keeping the laws the Creator designed for their benefit. Just as in the days of Noah, there will be a skeptical, rebellious majority who will choose their own destruction, rather than submit and live under the protection of their Creator. These skeptics still exist even though the destructive power of water displayed during the flood is so easily observed in the earth's broken surface so visible today.

Even many believing scientists might struggle with the idea of investigating future geologic events using subtle clues in the scriptures. Their careers have been spent on how present geologic processes support the record in the book of Genesis of a past global flood where the earth was fully covered with water. And yet, in the future the scriptures describe, most vividly in the book of Revelation, that the earth is once again covered, but in the future by fire. So, would it not be reasonable to also conclude that geologic events will be associated with this final cleansing of the earth? During the flood, the Creator, in His mercy, provided safety aboard the ark that Noah built while the earth was cleansed. At the very end, the Creator's mercy will be the protection found only inside the holy city while the earth is again cleansed prior to its restoration.

The purpose of this book is only to begin to investigate the many warning signs in prophecy that use clear and understandable words to describe these events as possibly literal and occurring in the natural, physical creation. Its purpose is more than just a scientific investigation however, woven into it will be consistent encouragement for believers to trust in the mercy of the Creator. He has promised to provide protection during these coming catastrophes which will culminate in eventual rescue by Yeshua the Messiah.

To deny any natural causes for prophesied, literal events is as equally dangerous as to deny the supernatural. Such a denial would raise the question of whether the Creator has power over His creation. When one reads in the scriptures about the giving of the covenant at Mount Sinai for example, there is thunder, lightning, thick clouds, and earthquakes; all natural events with natural causes, and yet it is recorded that the Creator was heard speaking over this noise and commotion. Demonstrated at Sinai so certainly, was the Creator's power to cause natural events and also be heard over nature's chaos and noise. Natural and supernatural both work together to give glory back to the Creator. In addition to the mercy shown by giving advance warning of these events in prophecy, another reason for them is to encourage humanity to also give glory back to their Creator just as creation does.

...Fear God and give glory to Him, for the hour of His judgment has come; and worship Him who made heaven and earth, the sea and springs of water.
Revelation 14:7

It is not the purpose of this book to stoke fear of the coming apocalypse by sensationalizing these predicted events. Nor is it the purpose of this book to interpret every phrase in every prophetic passage as some are certainly symbolic while others escape geologic explanation. Non-literal interpretations will not be discussed in detail, although the possibility is recognized of dual fulfillments where the prophecy may also point to events in the spiritual realm.

Neither is it the purpose of the book to identify key political or religious figures or movements at the time of the end. Attempts at identification invariably lead to conflict because the interpretations often pit one faction against others; the current enemy being demonized with apocalyptic language. In contrast, it is hoped that anyone may read this book and obtain a clearer picture of the Creator's character of love and mercy. Whether you may be Christian, Jewish, Muslim, or other; this book is for you.

The primary focus of this book is the geology portrayed in Revelation, a first century Greek book whose author was John. He was a follower of Yeshua and both were from the tribe of Judah. Because this book was written within the context of previous prophetic scriptures, the earlier, parallel passages to which it alludes to must also be investigated in order to arrive at a more complete understanding. Therefore, this book will also take a deep dive into the Hebrew parallels in the Tanakh.

In warning of the coming catastrophes, the mercy of the Creator extends beyond the readers of these books to all those who claim Abraham as their father. The Quran as well, echoes these previous scriptures, giving credence to them and getting its context from them, in the same way that the Greek scriptures echo the Hebrew.

Indeed, the day of judgement is an appointed time, a day when the trumpet will sound and you will come forward in multitudes, when the sky is opened and becomes wide portals, and the mountains are removed as if they were a mirage.
An Naba 78:17-20

This book begins with a discussion on why mercy requires the Creator to send these ominous warnings to all of humanity, and why they must be geologic: so that even those who have no scriptures will be warned.

The first section describes methods used to investigate both the scriptures and creation. Crucial geologic concepts will be clearly explained and a hypothesis formulated for what might be the initial cause that then results in the majority of the warning signs in Revelation being geologically fulfilled. One of the unique elements of this book is tying together the events predicted in prophecy rather than looking at each event individually.

The middle two sections discuss the seals, trumpets, and bowls recorded in Revelation. Section

II presents the seals as describing a chain reaction of natural consequences, possibly to begin with war over finite resources, like oil, and culminating in the death of many of the greedy wicked. Section III will present the trumpets and bowls as global geologic events such as impacts, earthquakes, and volcanic eruptions. Context from many parallel prophecies in the Hebrew scriptures will enhance understanding.

The final section deals with prophecies of the time of the end in the context of the geology of the Middle East. Historical accounts of geologic events in this land are used to bring these prophecies to life and discover where places of refuge may be found. The timing of these events relative to each other is discussed.

Finally, this book closes with a chapter that is a fictional recounting of what is previously described, pulling you into the predicted events so that they can be imagined for yourself. This captivating chapter can be read at any point while reading the rest of the book and you might just want to read it first!

It is my hope that by the time you come to the end of this book, you understand potential ways by which these dire warnings might literally occur so they may become less terrifying. The hypotheses or interpretations presented herein may be proven only partially accurate in the end. Far more important than the science is the trust and confidence in the love and mercy of the Creator that I am endeavoring to encourage. He will provide protection for those who follow His laws and trust in His Messiah: the rescuer who is coming very soon…

The Mercy of Catastrophe
Chapter 1

Humanity is being conditioned to fear the end of the world. Hollywood feeds this fear with terrifying imaginings of destruction. Politicians use this fear to acquire supporters and drive them into conflict with other groups; each with competing ideas of how to avoid catastrophe. Religious teachers also use fear to promote various means of salvation that only they can provide, often portraying other groups as the cause of coming judgement. Money is made by thus promoting fear. While terrifying catastrophes are predicted in the scriptures, neither those writings nor this book promote fear; at least not for the followers of Yeshua who are awaiting rescue. As you read this book, hope should replace the fear for the future that is promoted by religious and political propaganda, or disguised as entertainment.

So what is the purpose of the predicted signs of the end of the world given in prophecy? Are they a punishment sent by a vengeful deity bent on some kind of perverse justice? Or, are they simply warning signs designed in such a way that the warning is amplified so that all have a chance of hearing and heeding, even those without scripture? Alongside the prophecies of catastrophe are many recorded promises of protection which show that there is a safe path toward ultimate rescue. Because promises are included, it may be clearly seen that the purpose of the prophecies is not to instill fear, but rather to only give advance warning.

But are the catastrophes themselves actually a mercy sent by the Creator? The answer requires an evaluation of why there are certain catastrophes predicted and not others. In this book there are two kinds of catastrophes that will be discussed: natural consequences and global geologic warnings.

Natural consequences are not warnings sent in mercy by the Creator. They are simply the result of actions taken by humanity. If a miner knocks down the support columns in a mine, the mine will collapse on top of him because of the law of gravity. Death by crushing is not a punishment for removing supports, it is a consequence of the choice to do so. In Section II, the seals of Revelation are presented as a chain reaction of natural consequences caused by human choices. For example, the choice to go to war, which destroys resources, naturally leads to famine and a lack of proper nutrition allows pestilences to spread.

Of greater concern is whether the geologic catastrophes predicted are vengeful punishments or warnings sent as a mercy. The catastrophes dealt with in Section III include impacts of celestial objects on earth, increasing earthquakes, and also volcanic eruptions. Why might these warnings be geologic and not simply loud trumpet blasts for example?

Over time, and increasingly rapidly, humanity is being transformed into a society without morality, where the truth is subjective rather than absolute. A leading cause is the indoctrination into a pseudo-scientific religion where the main tenet is the "theory" of evolution. This "theory" proposes that the origin of life is due to random chance rather than purposeful design direct from the hand of the loving Creator. Laws and truth are the basis upon which creation operates. Random chance however, cannot evolve any organized, logical laws, nor the singular, internal consistency of absolute truth. Logic dictates that these must be designed by the Creator as part of His creation. By promoting random chance as the origin of life, morality and truth become subjectively self-determined on an individual basis and society becomes what it is today.

Because random chance will never result in such complexity, those who promote it must appeal to vast eons of time to make it seem more plausible. It is claimed that, given enough vast time, beneficial changes will randomly build on each other, resulting in the complexity that now exists. One of the main supports for the "theory" of evolution is the supposed deep time derived from geology. The principle of using present processes to better understand what has happened in the past is a valid and geologic principle that may even be used to shed light on the future, as this book proposes. These are both entirely logical starting premises that are easily tested and shown to be true by comparing geologic processes happening now, to known geologic events of a few years ago, or by making predictions that may be observed to happen in the near future.

The problem arises when this principle is used subjectively and inconsistently by those with an agenda. A scientist sitting at the bottom of a canyon beside a trickling river in late summer, could observe the rate at which the water slowly erodes away the rock and publish the false conclusion that it must have required millions upon millions of years to form the canyon. If the scientist were to observe the river during the spring floods, where fast-moving water is pounding rock against rock, the conclusion for the time that it takes to erode the canyon would be far shorter. After the eruption of Mount Saint Helens, it was observed that thick layers of mud and ash may be deposited and deep canyons then carved within just a few days. Still, the majority of geologists cling to the false conclusions of gradual geologic change as proof for millions of years, either willfully ignoring evidence of the contrary, or in-excusably ignorant of its existence. Those who recognize and teach the truth are so few in number that most of humanity is left hearing only the preaching of this naive pseudo-science that is just a religion without morals where truth is subjective.

Because supposed geologic evidence for slow, gradual processes is such a necessary support for this religion, the coming warnings must be in the form of geologic catastrophes. The only way to expose these lies is with their opposite: the truth. With each new event: earthquake, eruption, or flood; cracks open wider in the dam that is hindering the progress of knowledge and which must, and will come crashing down. Such ignorance is captive to human experience and so each new catastrophe is a crack forming, leading to certain collapse of false thinking and the flooding realization of the truth. Observations of future events, just like Mount Saint Helens, will be used to expose the frailty of this flawed "scientific" propaganda that is being forced on humanity.

Geologic catastrophes are now occurring with increasing severity and frequency; events like the tsunami in Indonesia in 2004 and the earthquake in Turkey in 2023. Seeing these events happen to their own home villages, humanity may now visualize for themselves how greater catastrophic events in the past—like the global flood—shaped the earth much more rapidly than they were taught. Catastrophes to come will yet powerfully demonstrate that geologic processes are not uniformly slow and gradual. Thus the only logical conclusion is that the earth is far too young for evolution to have had enough time to occur and that life must have been created.

Such occurrences are trumpet-like warnings designed to amplify trust in the scriptures, both the authenticity of historical events recorded, and also the future events predicted. They are precisely what mercy requires to lead all humanity to acknowledge their Creator and source of life. He is the only One capable of sustaining life and so it is imperative to bring as many as possible closer to Him, while also exposing the lies that He did not create everything and does not exist.

In the supposed absence of the Creator, who sets laws and defines truth, everyone becomes their own god. Because in this religion everyone is their own highest authority, setting laws and defining truth for oneself, it places every human that adheres to this thinking in competition with everyone else. Life becomes a vicious fight for the survival of the fittest. Because there is greater safety in groups, humanity segregates into political and religious factions with various moral ideologies that their individuals believe are the most advantageous. With nothing else to hope for beyond this life, selfish pleasures become paramount and the earth's few resources are rapidly depleted. As these resources become more scarce, hatred between groups increases as prejudices are found to be a useful tool to deepen divisions and thus drive the population to conflict. Genocide and extinction is the inevitable result; likely even before all the resources are fully consumed.

Breaking down the illusions upon which this false religion is based, by using increasingly-severe geologic catastrophes is a mercy! As these warnings reach a mighty crescendo, humanity will coalesce into only two groups. The majority will fight, clinging to their self-made god status and irrationally ignoring that the lies are collapsing upon which their religion is based. The alternative is to join with the remnant who turn towards the Creator who created them and choose to trust in His love and mercy. At the end, both groups will be undeniably confronted with the reality of the Creator. He is the only Source and Sustainer of life, and without Him, humanity will not survive what is coming. As all life on earth becomes unsustainable, the warnings given to the entire earth are an opportunity to chose whether or not to be rescued.

The soon-coming catastrophes are not sent by an angry deity bent on vengeance, punishment, or some other form of perverse justice. Rather, they are sent as warnings with a dual purpose. As the wicked turn on each other in violence and the scale of genocide rapidly increases, natural catastrophes will also increase as creation rejects this bloodshed. The murderous rampaging of these wolves will be hindered by the predicted geologic catastrophes. For others, the catastrophes serve the same purpose as the bark of the sheep dog. The bark is used to get the sheep together into the sheepfold where they will be safe and protected. A remnant will acknowledge that there is a Creator after witnessing catastrophe and turn towards Him. This remnant is as yet, scattered around the world. Many do not know there is a Creator, much less His character of love and mercy. Those who chose to imitate this character, exemplified by Yeshua the Messiah, will be drawn together for survival while they await their rescue, all the while under the protection of their Creator.

But He made His own people go forth like sheep, and guided them in the wilderness like a flock; and He led them on safely, so that they did not fear; but the sea overwhelmed their enemies. Psalm 78:52-53

SCIENTIFIC METHODS OF SCRIPTURE STUDY
Section I

The mountains rose;
the valleys sank down
to the place which You
established for them.

Psalm 104:8
(NASB®)

Parallels on Puzzle Pieces
Chapter 2

As a geoscientist, I practice the art of what might be termed three-dimensional thinking. This method for thinking requires intimate familiarity of detailed data or concepts. Over time, the patterns observed are gradually compiled and may then be summarized for others. The skills of being able to recognize patterns and then communicate what is learned are skills that most anyone may acquire and practice by patiently investigating any topic, either in creation or the scriptures and then sharing one's discoveries.

During my career in the petroleum industry, I routinely sifted through data from thousands of well bores identifying recognizable patterns, correlating them, and then sharing summaries of what was discovered. Often the information collected was portrayed on maps which were then shown to company decision-makers in order to convince them to spend millions of dollars to drill a new oil or gas well in a specific place.

When it comes to the scriptures, I use a similar approach. Over time, familiarizing myself with many verses and investigating those that contain similar words and phrases. In this way, new understandings naturally emerge from verses that were meant to be interpreted together. This book may be read like a map that I am sharing with you, so that you may come to your own conclusions.

Almost everyone is capable of assembling puzzles and the process is similar. Adjacent wells or parallel verses are like puzzle pieces that are mostly similar with a few subtle differences from one to the next. For puzzles, pieces with similar colors should first be grouped, such as all the yellow pieces with brown spots for example. Visual pattern analysis is what is used to identify major similar features. Subtle details are then investigated which determine if the pieces are adjacent. Large brown spots might be part of a neck, while smaller brown spots might be from a hip. Upon completion, an interlocking picture of a gangly giraffe emerges.

Assembling puzzles is rarely a rapid process; one must carefully observe the details of many pieces, not only a few. A place for a piece may not be found right away, and so it might be abandoned for a time on the far side of the table while other pieces are assembled. At times, a friend might be the one to hand over a needed piece from across the table. While puzzles may be satisfying, an even deeper satisfaction may be had when scriptures that have been investigated for awhile lock beautifully together.

As the human brain acquires knowledge, it does so in much the same fashion as assembling a puzzle. New ideas may be easier to recall if they are locked into an existing framework instead of forgotten on the mental table. When a new word is being learned, that sounds similar to one already known, or if it may be linked to an existing piece of knowledge, or a special memory; then it is much more easily recorded into the network of neurons already existing in the brain.

Neurons connect to many thousands of other neurons at special junctions called synapses, thus making this network three-dimensional. Synapses are much like the knobs and sockets of a puzzle piece and are created every time something new is learned. In essence, the physical layout of the brain mirrors the way the brain learns best; by locking ideas together like puzzle pieces and observing the completed picture.

When investigating subtle geologic clues in scripture, using a similar process is inherently messy, with scattered pieces found all over the mental table as the picture is being assembled. Putting together such puzzles is difficult and takes a great deal of time and effort, but the resulting picture is much easier to appreciate in the long run when its beauty is unveiled. If you give me the time to paint a picture for you over the time spent reading this book, I hope you will find what I share as comprehensible as a completed puzzle. Maybe you might join me in the excitement of discovery by adding a few puzzle pieces yourself.

The prophetic puzzles are certainly complex enough for many students to be investigating them. Interpretations may be made looking at many different facets; geoscience being just one of them. I must admit that more than once, a comment made by a fellow student of the scriptures has sparked something in my thinking that has helped me to continue working on my part of the prophetic puzzle. While they may be investigating their interests, my training as a geoscientist has better suited me to identify subtle clues in prophecy related to events in the physical, natural creation.

Before puzzles are first cut apart, the picture is complete and the same is true of prophecy. The Creator, who knows the future, has cut apart what is plain to Him and given the pieces, or even multiple pieces, from this picture of future events, to various prophets. These puzzle pieces often became more fragmented on being transmitted to us. Everything the prophets saw or heard may not have been fully recorded or described for us in writing.

For example, what John saw in vision was clear and yet, the words he had to describe what he saw were not adequate. He did not have the technical language of modern geoscience. He may have seen an asteroid falling to earth, but without that technical word, he was left with only the ability to describe it as like a star falling to earth. Even if he could have described it more fully, remember that words do not convey all the details that the eyes see or the ears hear.

Although John was certainly not trained in modern geoscience, he was trained in the writings of earlier prophets. He lived in a religious culture that was fully immersed in their writings. He was intimately familiar with these writings because of his own dedication to their study. So when it came time for him to write what he also saw, he would have chosen the same descriptive words or phrases that they had also used.

The method of linking together parallel words and phrases from one prophet's writings to another's is a valid method because it replicates how those prophets recorded what they saw and heard. When it comes to later verses, the use of parallel words and phrases tell us which of the previous verses of scripture a prophet had in mind when they recorded their part of the puzzle. For each of the later prophets, their context was the writings of even earlier prophets. Each successive prophet has repeated similar basic information as well as unique, additional details. The Creator sent similar visions, with the same message, to many different prophets spanning history and geography. This broad dispersion of the message by the Creator shows His mercy by ensuring the message was transmitted most effectively.

Allow me to describe for you how this method of linking parallel verses may be described as using three-dimensional thinking. As my goal for this book is to avoid theological topics as much as possible, I will use an example that hopefully is not too controversial. This example's first puzzle piece has on it a verse from the prophet Daniel with the Hebrew word [תמיד] *tamiyd* on it which means continual, or daily.

And from the time that the daily [tamiyd] sacrifice is taken away, and the abomination of desolation is set up… Daniel 12:11

The word "*sacrifice*" was added here by the translators to explain the *tamiyd* and it is not found in the original Hebrew. This word was likely added because the word *tamiyd* is also used to describe

24

certain sacrifices prescribed in the Torah as revealed to a previous prophet: Moses.

Now this is what you shall offer on the altar: two lambs of the first year, day by day continually [tamiyd]. Exodus 29:38.

However, this is just one of the many facets of what the *tamiyd* is, and so I would term stopping here, with only linking two parallel verses as linear, or two-dimensional thinking. The word *tamiyd* has such greater depth to it. With further investigation, it is found that sacrifice was not the only daily, continual ritual performed in the sanctuary services as laid out in the Torah. The word *tamiyd* shows up for the very first time in the command to place the bread on the table in the sanctuary.

And you shall set the showbread on the table before Me always [tamiyd]. Exodus 25:30.

The seven-branched lamp was lit (Exodus 27:20). The high priest dressed in special garments including a breastplate and turban (Exodus 28:29 & 38). Incense was burnt in the morning and evening (Exodus 30:7-8). Each of these verses commands that these rituals be done *tamiyd*. Water washings had to be performed before entering the sanctuary to do these rituals, meaning washings were also done *tamiyd* even though the word is not mentioned specifically. Later, it is recorded that trumpets were also blown *tamiyd* (1 Chronicles 16:6).

In all, there are at least seven things that are being done *tamiyd* and sacrifice is but one. It should be rather apparent then, that by inserting the word "*sacrifice*" into Daniel's writings after *tamiyd* that the translators have thus limited our understanding of what Daniel was trying to convey. Now, instead of a typical four-sided puzzle piece, this puzzle piece already has seven sides to it with more to discover.

In order to build out of the two dimensional plane however, additional concepts may be linked to each of these aspects of *tamiyd*. Yeshua speaks to us that he is the "*bread of life*" (John 6:35) and the "*light of the world*" (John 8:12). David sings that our prayers and praises rise like incense and sacrifices (Psalm 141:2). The Creator also covers us with the "*garments of salvation*" (Isaiah 61:10) and "*cleanses us from all unrighteousness*" (1 John 1:9).

Hopefully by using this three-dimensional method you may begin to see that the word *tamiyd* encapsulates the continual, daily relationship of every believer with the Creator. Performing the *tamiyd* is just as necessary for life as daily meals are. The purpose of these sanctuary rituals were to teach us how to enter into this heavenly, life-giving relationship. *Tamiyd* is such a beautiful, multi-faceted diamond of a word and our relationship with our Creator would be very desolate without what it describes being put into practice.

Tamiyd is just one of the details, just one of the colors, on our puzzle piece containing the above verse from Daniel and it is quite the beautiful handful to deal with. Some words are just not as unique as *tamiyd* however, and so whole phrases might be investigated in a similar fashion.

In the example of *tamiyd*, and throughout my investigation of Hebrew or Greek words, I may use a wide range of verses to help better understand a word based on its usage in context. I will not however, invent new, strange meanings for words which are not present in either widely accepted translations, or widely used dictionaries. What may be new will be how the words investigated are applied or understood.

Two-dimensional thinking might appear more logical and simple in that it builds linearly, one element after the next. However, the problem with stopping there is that the full beauty is not seen. A great deal of additional information might be missed, and it is easier to arrive at a conclusion that is only partial at best. At worst, the conclusion reached overlooks critical subtle clues making the proposed interpretation incorrect. Utilizing three-dimensional thinking provides a greater depth to understanding. There are more connections that interlock such interpretations together which makes them less prone to failure and gives a more solid foundation. If you begin to practice three-dimensional thinking on your own, I think you will come to understand how valuable it is.

For the entirety of this book, my method will be to first identify parallel words or phrases of scripture that may be subtle clues of something occurring in the physical, natural creation. Certain words and phrases stand out to me that appear to describe geologic processes. I will be looking at scripture through the same set of eyes I have used previously as a geoscientist. And yes, these eyes do have a bias.

Before I ever trained as a geoscientist, I decided that my bias would be to believe that my Creator has power over creation and influences natural events to accomplish His purposes. I have two eyes. My first eye was trained from my youth to look at creation believing in a Creator. My other eye was trained later to see in science. Whether I am looking at creation in the natural world, or prophecy in the scriptures, it is my hope that by looking at either, with both eyes open, that I may have better depth perception and discover the harmonious truth.

After compiling many parallel scriptures together, my purpose is to present the simplest, most literal interpretation of prophecy. I do not wish to diminish the importance of interpreting prophecy symbolically in the spiritual realm, it is just that my focus will be the physical, which is often a reflection of the spiritual, heavenly reality. What has, will, or is going on in the spiritual realm is of course far more significant than what happens on earth. I believe that what occurs in the physical realm is just a mirror of what happens in the spiritual. This book however, is limited to the geologic interpretation of prophecy.

After describing multiple clues presented in the following chapters, my hope is to put together some of the puzzle pieces so that you also might see a beautiful, encouraging picture of the Creator's power over creation and His mercy, not just in the past in Genesis, but in the future predicted by Revelation and other prophetic writings as well.

Geo-Eschatology
Chapter 3

There are some geologic concepts discussed in this book that need to be explained. To make their explanation more interesting, I will at the same time be walking you down the same journey the Creator took me in my previous studies. By the end of this journey, you should be able to see that I am well qualified to write about these topics.

First, geology is primarily an observational science, and it is only an experimental science in some cases. Experimental science is what is taught in most schools where the scientific method goes something like this: first, ask a question and then propose possible answers to the question called hypotheses. Second, design an experiment to test the hypotheses to see which are false. Collect data from the experiments, analyze the data, and finally draw conclusions about which hypotheses fail. The goal is to determine which hypotheses are possible. Science should never conclude that any given hypothesis is true, only possible, simply because there is always a possibility that unknown variables might change the outcome of the experiment.

Chemistry, physics, and biology are each examples of experimental sciences. Scientists may design experiments where compounds are mixed together, the effects of zero-gravity are tested, or the number of plants living in an area are increased after testing different growing methods. Most of the time, these sciences study present processes primarily by direct experimentation.

Geology however, is more often the indirect study of the past. Studies of the past are based on present observation, models, and comparison much like a crime scene investigator. Forensic science is the process that detectives use to compare observations from a crime scene to a similar model to reach a conclusion. They might take a cadaver and use various types of blades on it, then compare the cut marks they made with the cut marks on the victim to attempt to determine the type of murder weapon used. The cadaver of course is only a model for a living body and the cuts on each might be slightly different.

Models are heavily used in the study of past processes on the earth. For example, a structural geologist like myself, might uses a press to crush a small rock sample and observe how artificial fractures in the rock are created. The results from the model may then be compared to fractures created by natural processes in order to test the hypotheses about how fractures form. Geologic processes often occur at a much larger scale than what may be modeled, and so there is always the possibility of subtle differences that cannot be accounted for in a lab. There is a bit of an art to geoscience and some speculation as it is just not as concrete as other sciences.

The curiosity of the unknown is what sparked my interest in the continual opportunities to discover subtleties and solve the complex puzzles found in geology. As a child on frequent hikes, I was taught to appreciate the Creator's "second book" as found in the creation. As I became a teenager, I wanted to understand how the events of a global flood may have occurred, as described in the book of Genesis. I wanted to understand how science supported the scriptures.

I began my investigation of geoscience by helping believing scientists conduct their field studies. These scientists, who believed in a recent creation and global flood, taught me the logic of how to think scientifically. Their mentoring helped me to re-evaluate for myself the assumptions required to interpret the raw data that is used to somehow support the "theory" of evolution. Their training laid a strong foundation for independent thinking.

I obtained a Master of Science in Geoscience from Colorado State University where I was given the opportunity to pursue my interest in structural geology. In simple terms, structural geology is the four-dimensional investigation of deformation within rocks that come in the form of fractures, such as faults, and folds, and the timing of this deformation.

During an internship with the company that paid for my research stipend, I was able to collect fracture data from gas wells and other subsurface data in one of their fields in central Wyoming. I then followed this up with a few months hiking all over the nearby mountains collecting additional fracture data in rocks exposed at the surface.

Fractures in rock are created because of stress and come in two forms: joints which are simple breaks in the rock like rifts, and faults which are breaks where the rock on either side moves, slipping past each other in opposite directions. There are three types of faults: strike-slip faults, like the San Andreas in California, in which blocks of land move past each other horizontally along a near vertical fault; sloping normal faults, such as on either side of the Dead Sea, which result in blocks, like that under the floor of the sea, dropping relative to the surrounding mountains; or reverse faults in which blocks are pushed up over other blocks as they slip along ramp-like faults to form mountains like the Rockies that I studied in western North America.

The stress that causes these fractures has three axes: the direction from which the maximum stress acts on the rock, an intermediate axis, and a minimum; all perpendicular to each other. In the case of reverse faults, the maximum compressive stress is horizontal pushing the rock together, and the least compressive stress is vertical, allowing the mountains to rise higher. For normal faulting, the axes are opposite and the least compressive stress is horizontal. This allows the earth's crust to extend as blocks of land rift and move apart. Where there are predominately normal faults and rifts the geologic setting is extensional, while areas that have mostly reverse faults are compressional because the crust is being pushed together.

Sometimes it is difficult to identify the type of fault, especially older, inactive faults. In such places the type and orientation of small-scale fractures may be observed in exposed rock at the surface, giving clues as to the stresses that caused slip on larger, more major faults in the area. Also, the timing of when certain stress regimes were active may be determined by looking at the relative sequence of formation of the rocks and their later fracturing.

My study area contained rocks from the oldest to the youngest in the geologic column, spanning earth's history. In the older rocks I found small reverse faults. These reverse faults were not found in the younger rocks, only numerous normal faults. Because normal faults form during stress that is extensional, the opposite of compressional, this indicates that during some period in earth's history, the mountains surrounding my study area stopped being pushed together upwards, and instead began to collapse—sliding back down on the older faults. Compression followed by extension.

No other stress regimes could be identified in the data collected in that region. This lack of evidence for additional stress regimes throughout history should be very concerning for any geologist who believes that the geologic column spans millions of years. Given such vast supposed time, one should logically conclude that there would be multiple cyclic episodes where mountains were rising only to collapse and rise again on endless repeat.

A single event where the mountains rose and the valleys sank is consistent with the record in the scriptures of a global flood during the time of Noah. I believe that compressional stresses within the earth's crust were used to raise up the continents creating both mountains and deep ocean basins. This provided a way to drain off the flood waters and expose dry land once again. This flood would have been an awesomely catastrophic event associated with major faulting and subsequent earthquakes and volcanism. Geologic evidence for such a great upheaval is strikingly visible in the rugged mountain chains and canyons all over the earth.

The structural history of central Wyoming that I discovered, is just a single evidence among the thousands in all the sciences supporting the record of a global flood in Genesis. When I began studying geology, I had hoped to find the ultimate proof of the Creator's power over creation. What I found instead however, was the weight of many evidences so numerous, logical, and convincing, that I was left to conclude that the only reason some believe in the wild, unsubstantiated "theory" of evolution was because they wanted to.

By the time I finished graduate school, I saw the reason why many choose to disbelieve the scriptures: it is because they want an excuse to continue a rebellious, lawless lifestyle. Because there is logically a Creator, then they should keep the laws He designed for their benefit. Laws of gravity being no different than laws of morality. The only other option is to deny the existence of the Creator, as without Him, there would then be no requirement to follow His laws.

Disillusioned with humanity, I decided on a career in the petroleum industry instead of pursuing a more academic career dedicated to promoting creationism. While working oil and gas fields from the Canadian to the Mexican borders I discovered further evidence that there was only one single mountain building episode spanning the geologic column. The results of my investigations were published in a peer-reviewed publication and also presented at industry conferences and gatherings of young earth creationists. But my work is only one small evidence.

The amount of work that has gone into studying the book of Genesis from a geologic perspective is phenomenal. There is a handful of dedicated geologists whose career has been to compile and promote hundreds of evidences supporting a recent creation and global flood. This evidence is out there for anyone willing to look at it honestly. What has been lacking until now, as the time of the end approaches, is a geologic look into the future and the book of Revelation.

Of course humanity does not know what the future holds, so the whole idea of investigating geology in the future would be ridiculous if there was no way to pull back the curtains of time and unveil glimpses of what may happen. Fortunately, our Creator is full of mercy for His creation and has given warnings of what is to come that were faithfully recorded by the prophets and preserved for us today. In addition to geologic investigations of creation followed by catastrophe in the book of beginnings: Genesis; the final book: Revelation, predicts catastrophe followed by re-creation.

In the book of Revelation, the Greek word translated "*God*" is [θεός] *theos* and it appears 99 times, more than any other noun. Theology is the study of God, or words about God, the suffix derived from the Greek word [λόγος] *logos*. The second most common noun in Revelation is [γῆ] *ge* which means earth and appears 82 times. Combining *ge* and *logos* gives us geology! Seeing as how words about the earth are so central to Revelation, I hope you would agree that a trained geoscientist is indeed qualified to investigate this book right alongside theologians. The Creator has two ways of revealing Himself, His scriptures, and His creation. Being able to connect the two together is necessary to discover the harmonious whole of truth revealed in both. For truth to be true, it must be singular and only present where there is harmony.

For the literal, physical events predicted in the scriptures to be fulfilled, they must not happen in empty space, but on earth, to earth; the domain of geoscientists, not theologians. The term for the investigation of words about final geologic events might be properly termed geo-eschatology. It is the investigation, from a geologic perspective, of literal, physical events that may be found in prophetic writings describing the time of the end. This science should be an observational science whose focus is on comparing subtle textual clues in the scriptures with processes in the physical, natural world.

One of the ultimate goals of science is to be able to predict. A chemist should be able to warn you what would happen if certain chemicals are mixed together. A biologist should be able to warn you what would happen if ecological diversity is compromised. Then why should geoscientists be relegated to only describing the past? Geologic predictions, even those made by the prophets, should also be fully investigated.

The mercy of the Creator was demonstrated in predicting the soon coming of the global geologic catastrophe by water and safety was provided in the ark Noah built. The Creator will not fail at the time of the end to demonstrate His mercy once again in warning about, and rescuing those who trust and believe in Him from the final geologic catastrophes of fire. Future safety will ultimately be found inside the holy city that is to come.

For those who have chosen not to believe in the overwhelming evidence for the Creator's hand of mercy in Genesis, the warning signs predicted in Revelation are an additional opportunity to repent. Those who would survive must turn from rejecting their Creator, source and sustainer of life. They must submit to keeping the laws of love that He designed for humanity's benefit, if they desire to ultimately be rescued by the Messiah from certain death as these catastrophes reach their culmination.

Say to them: "As I live," says YHWH God, "I have no pleasure in the death of the wicked, but that the wicked turn from his way and live. Turn, turn from your evil ways! For why should you die. O house of Israel?" Ezekiel 33:11

Hearts Failing for Fear
Chapter 4

In Yeshua's prophecy, given on the Mount of Olives, he talks about events that will occur on earth before he returns, and also about what will happen in the heavens. It is possible that he was referring to the spiritual, heavenly realm in which the angels dwell. However, prophecy has many facets and the purpose of this book is to investigate the literal and physical facets. Events happening in the spiritual heavens would certainly have an impact on the earth, just as it is also possible that physical events in the physical heavens would have an impact on the earth as well.

These words of Yeshua, which are expanded upon and paralleled in Revelation, are first recorded by his followers, Matthew, Mark, and Luke. They all use the Greek word [οὐρανός] *ouranos*, meaning the visible heavens: the sky and atmosphere, or even the starry heavens. Because the word may also be applied to the spiritual heavens, the context from the verses is crucial. Of these three, Luke seems to be particularly fascinated by the predicted events in the heavens as he recorded additional words of Yeshua that the others did not.

...the powers in the heavens [ouranos] will be shaken.... Heaven [ouranos] and earth [ge] will pass away... Matthew 24:29 & 35, Mark 13:25 & 31, & Luke 21:26 & 33

...there will be fearful sights and great signs from heaven [ouranos].... men's hearts failing them from fear and the expectation of those things which are coming on the earth... Now when these things begin to happen, look up and lift up your heads, because your redemption draws near. Luke 21:11, 26 & 28

In these prophecies of Yeshua, the verses that are repeated in the three gospel records state that the "*heavens will be shaken*" and finally "*will pass away*". These phrases do not describe common occurrences that are easily understood. How are the heavens also shaken and how may life be sustained when heaven passes away? The spiritual heavens certainly do not "*pass away*", so it must refer to either the atmosphere, which all life breathes, or to the starry heavens. If it refers to the starry heavens, or space, then how again might the universe and life continue to exist without the sun for example? These are excellent questions that this book attempts to answer by combining scriptures and science using the methods described in the second chapter. The parallel wording of earlier Hebrew prophets will also be investigated to help better understand what Yeshua meant.

The additional verses from Luke faithfully record the encouragement of Yeshua to look up. Something will happen that will be visible and precede the rescue of the righteous. Clearly, Yeshua was not primarily referring to the spiritual, unseen realm, even if his words could be interpreted that way. Rather, his main focus was on the physical atmosphere or possibly the starry heavens. He states there will be "*great signs from heaven*" which will cause many hearts to fail "*from fear*". The stress and panic caused by such fear may actually result in too many steroids or hormones being produced by the human body, thus leading to increased risk of the heart stopping and death.

But these heavenly warning signs were not just described as stationary in the starry heavens, the verse records that they are moving toward the earth. The reason for the panic is given as "*the expectation of those things which are coming on the earth*". This is translated from the Greek phrase [προσδοκίας τῶν ἐπερχομένων τῇ οἰκουμένῃ] *prosdokias ton eperchomenon te oikoumene*. These five Greek words could also be translated with just five English words as: awaiting things arriving to earth.

In both Matthew and Mark it is recorded that Yeshua makes reference to only one type of celestial object that moves from heaven and arrives to earth. The Greek word is [ἀστήρ] aster, from which is derived a star in English. It also forms the root of the word asteroid, the suffix of the word, oid, is also from the Greek and means like. Asteroid literally means star-like. Asteroids may be just what these verses are describing.

> *...the stars [aster] will fall from heaven...*
> Matthew 24:29

> *The stars [aster] of heaven will fall... Mark 13:25*

Hollywood is obsessed with producing movies about massive asteroids wiping out life on earth. As the stories typically play out, scientists will discover that an asteroid is headed for earth and humanity panics. Many die even before the asteroid hits as humanity devolves into chaos and desperately tries to save itself. YouTube is full of "theories" of even more frightening rogue planets hitting the earth. These outlandish ideas do not fit the definition of a truly scientific theory as they have no basis in any observed reality, but they still gain views because they are sensational and entertaining.

This terrifying propaganda certainly gives a horrifying portrayal of something similar to what Yeshua may be talking about. However, Yeshua is encouraging believers, while the propaganda is designed to condition most to instead respond with absolute panic. Yeshua tells believers to "*look up*" because their "*redemption draws near*". Humanity is already looking up at the heavens in panic and Yeshua is telling his followers to also look up, look again, and keep looking, because their rescue is coming soon.

These "*great signs from heaven*" are sent from the Creator as a mercy to warn those who dwell on the earth that Yeshua is coming soon to rescue his followers. Instead of heeding these warning signs, the wicked refuse to believe in the Creator's mercy. Fear and panic will drive them to attempt their own salvation, on their own terms. They should rather trust in the promises of rescue for those who keep the laws designed by the Creator for their own benefit. Only those who follow Yeshua's example to keep the Creator's laws of love will be rescued.

Warning signs at the time of the end are not the punishments of an vengeful deity, but they might instead be the natural consequences of humanity's pride and vain attempts to save themselves. Imagine that scientists soon discover that a giant asteroid is headed towards earth. It appears that it is on a collision course, but of course, it might be a near miss; the probability of an impact is not certain. In Hollywood fantasies, nuclear devices are often used to divert apocalyptic-sized asteroids. Using such an approach in reality, maybe humanity will succeed in breaking it into a series of smaller pieces that hit the earth just as described in the second, third, and fifth trumpets of Revelation.

Or, this series of predicted impacts might be natural like the pieces of comet Shoemaker-Levy 9 that impacted Jupiter in 1994. What would be the geological consequences of such impacts, or even just the passing near to earth of a large object? Might the other geologic warnings described such as earthquakes, darkness, extreme heat, and floods; all be caused by such an object? How a celestial object or event may cause geologic catastrophes on earth is what will be investigated in Section III primarily.

This imagining is just speculation of course, but in science such potential explanations would be called hypotheses. Hypothesizing is the process of speculation or supposition, the logical proposition of possible explanations based on limited evidence; then used as a starting point for further investigation. While some could call the hypotheses in this book wild speculations, their very possibility unveils just how variable the interpretations and explanations for prophecy may be.

Evaluating multiple hypotheses, either literal or symbolic even, is a useful exercise in opening the mind to potential fulfillments of prophecy that may not otherwise be considered. Multiple hypotheses are proposed in science and tested in order to arrive at truth and not become fixated on a potentially false solution. Eschatology, as a pursuit of knowledge about the time of the end, is also a science and should use similar methods of evaluating and testing multiple hypotheses.

When it comes to prophecy, some may speculate, or really hypothesize, that much of it has already been fulfilled. Others, that it will be fulfilled only symbolically or spiritually. These are all valid hypotheses and none of them should be considered more speculative than the other. Only when there is the ability to look back at the end of earth's history will humanity know for sure which interpretations of prophecy were correct. Until the end, all possible interpretations should be considered.

Believers should be careful not to cling to absolute, unyielding opinions. No cause for division should come from differing opinions on prophetic speculation. History is riddled with examples where humanity thought that prophecy was being fulfilled and as yet, these same prophecies are still being interpreted today in new ways to give warning, hope, and encouragement.

The purpose of this book is not to evaluate theological hypotheses. It is rather an investigation of prophecy through the eyes of a trained, believing geoscientist. Therefore, certain topics such as the identity of the beasts, the two witnesses, or the 144,000 will be avoided. Focusing on identity leads to conflict between groups, while instead focusing on where is far more productive. Using geologic clues, allows believers to avoid those places where the wicked will be, whoever the wicked end up being.

The purpose of this book is only to investigate the logical possibility of a single hypothesis and its supporting, related hypotheses. At the end of the book, the only conclusion should be whether what is described is possible, not certain, nor how likely. Even though there are multiple hypotheses for how prophecy is fulfilled, this book will not evaluate them as there are simply to many. Instead of looking at the many individual interpretations of prophecies, this book attempts to discover a unifying interpretation that interlocks many prophecies together and thus paints a more complete picture.

This chapter has just the first few of the many verses investigated throughout this book. Already subtle clues for impacts of celestial objects on earth may be seen. The overarching hypothesis presented in this book is that a large asteroid, or other celestial event, is the root cause of many signs in prophecy being geologically fulfilled; in particular the signs in Revelation. The purpose of this book is to convey this hypothesis in such as way as to show more of the mercy of the Creator.

Several of the warning signs of Revelation describe the geologic activity resulting from celestial objects striking the earth. As such, it is very easy to conceive of the possibility of yet another, a fourth celestial object, just missing the earth, but passing near enough to gravitationally pull on the earth. The earth moving closer to the sun is presented in this book as the mechanism by which many warning signs in Revelation are geologically fulfilled. If the earth moving closer to the sun is caused by the passing of a celestial object, or series of objects, then asteroids are much more likely given their rocky composition which gives them a greater density and gravitational pull. Comets are far less likely because they are primarily composed of low density ice.

As I am not an astrophysicist, I cannot say for certain whether an asteroid is capable of pulling the earth into a closer orbit to the sun. It could very well be that some of the sun's energy could be converted to mass, pulling all the planets closer; a tear could form in the gravitational fabric of space; or some other celestial event would be required—whether understood or today considered supernatural. From a geologic perspective, the exact celestial cause is less important than the consequences of an orbital shift which will be dealt with in detail in Section III and is the main focus of this book. Revelation itself does not focus on what happens in the heavens as much as it does what happens on earth; the domain of humanity. Whatever the root cause, Revelation appears to be describing a natural sequence of geologic events that includes more severe and frequent earthquakes, increasing volcanic activity, extreme heat, and flooding due to sea level rise.

If the majority of these warnings in Revelation have a single root cause, then that implies that the Creator is allowing the least amount of catastrophe required to adequately warn humanity and is not pouring out punishments on the earth many times over. The question to ask ourselves is if we believe the Creator to be a vengeful deity, bent on punishing and destroying His creation, or, if He is full of mercy in protecting those who keep His laws of love, trust in the Messiah's soon coming rescue, and seek the safety found only in the presence of the only Source and Sustainer of life. It is for us to decide what we choose to believe about the character of the Creator when these natural catastrophes begin to happen all around us.

Cast your burden upon YHWH and He will sustain you; He will never allow the righteous to be shaken.
Psalm 55:22 (NASB®)

OPENED SEALS AS
NATURAL CONSEQUENCES
Section II

For thus says YHWH God of Israel:
"The bin of flour shall not be used up,
nor shall the jar of oil run dry…"

1 Kings 17:14

Less Oil a Catalyst for War
Chapter 5

While the primary purpose of this book is to investigate the hypothesis that many of the signs are fulfilled geologically, there are other prophetic events that might also be investigated from the perspective of a geoscientist. This section deals with the seven seals of Revelation 6-8:1 while the next section will deal with the seven trumpets and seven bowls. The seals describe disasters that are the consequences of humanity's wicked choices to go to war or oppress others economically, while the trumpets and bowls describe natural catastrophes such as impacts and earthquakes. Humanity may neither initiate natural catastrophes, nor prevent them, but some disasters are caused by humanity's choices.

War is the most obvious of these disasters and often causes subsequent deadly disasters such as economic turmoil, famine, and pestilence. This is exactly the same sequence of events described when seals two, three, and four are opened and the horsemen ride forth. Rather than the punishments of an angry deity, each seal is the natural consequence of human choice; a chain reaction of events that begins with war. In His mercy, the Creator brings these natural consequences to an end when Yeshua returns to rescue the righteous when the sixth and seventh seals are opened.

The cause of most wars is competition over limited, naturally occurring resources like oil or gold.

Because of resource scarcity, geoscientists have a very critical role in the process of exploring for, and efficiently extracting energy and mineral resources from the earth. Some, who understand the impact of their efforts on coming trends in economics and politics should be considered well-qualified to share their foresight in much the same way a weather-worn rancher would have valuable insight into the future price of beef. As available resources dwindle, these geoscientists may find themselves on the front lines of growing turmoil; I certainly have.

At first, co-workers begin to compete over the dwindling number of economically viable projects to work on. Eventually this spills over to the community as corporations consolidate, let go of workers, and shut down operations. If a country is large enough, or has an abundance of natural resources, these operations may move elsewhere. Eventually, even the largest countries, with the greatest access to natural resources, will begin to see increasing internal turmoil as their supply diminishes and needs become unfulfilled. There are thus two main reasons for most wars, the need for resources and the lust of those in power to maintain their top status by re-directing internal turmoil outwards.

Unfortunately, human greed and the desire for luxury and excess may lead countries into conflict with each other even before resources are depleted and turmoil ensues. Smaller countries are colonized with the excuse that their culture is uncivilized. The rhetoric against stronger competing countries is often framed in religious terms to inspire the masses to take up the fight.

All countries need energy in order for their economies to thrive and expand. This energy used to come in the form of human energy from slave labor, or from products grown from the earth, such as trees, that were burned for cooking and heating. Then, with the Industrial Revolution, humanity began to access the buried energy locked within the earth in the form fossil fuels like coal, oil, and natural gas.

Coal, closest to the surface, was the easiest to access and so became the first fossil fuel widely used. The cheap energy obtained from burning coal allowed humanity to build factories and infrastructure like railroads at the time of the Industrial Revolution. Factories powered by coal manufactured goods at a lower cost. Trains and steamboats transported those goods more rapidly. A higher quality of life for many was thus generated.

In America, the northern part of the country led the way in this industrialization. Their abundance of coal allowed the north the luxury of freeing slaves and promoting abolitionism. However, the economy of the southern part of the country was still driven by industrial-scale human energy in the form of mass slavery. This dichotomy was the main driver of the American Civil War, a war which probably would not have been fought even a few decades later as industrialization would have moved into the south, making slavery obsolete.

Even though coal is still used today, it was rapidly replaced by oil as the primary energy source. Oil contains much more energy than an equivalent volume of coal. This energy density makes it easier to transport and an ideal source of energy to power personal vehicles. Along with natural gas, it also has the added benefit of burning more cleanly than wood or coal resulting in less pollution. And so began the competition over the control of petroleum resources that continues today.

America, Britain, and Germany, produced significant amounts of coal, had advanced industrial economies, and eventually discovered that their coal resources were not limitless. Germany in particular lacked access to oil when compared to the other two powers. The need of the German economy to control sufficient resources was the main reason for the German invasion of neighboring countries towards the beginning of both world wars. The need for oil continues even today as a catalyst for conflict. Controlling oil resources is the reason for continued American imperialism and interference in places such as the Middle East.

Theoretically, the earth can continually form new resources of coal, oil, and gas, but the scale at which these could currently be made would be insufficient compared to their rate of consumption. Supposedly, these resources were continually and slowly generated over millions of years. So given enough time, these resources could be renewed, but the evidence for this is lacking and the assumptions made are faulty. Rather, the raw data better supports the hypothesis that these resources were formed once, during a single, catastrophic geologic event; the global flood recorded in the scriptures.

Studies show that much of the coal resources present today are the compressed remains of torn up rafts of vegetation, swept away by torrents of water and eventually buried in tremendous amounts of sediment. During the global flood, the "*fountains of the great deep*", as mentioned in Genesis 7:11, may have brought warm, subterranean waters to the surface. Warm water, full of the decaying bodies of plants and animals, would have provided the perfect environment for blooms of algae and bacteria.

It is widely accepted in the petroleum industry that petroleum is primarily the product of algae and bacteria that has been buried by sediment to great depths. Pressure and heat at these depths are what converts organic material into molecules of oil, and at higher temperatures and pressures, into gas. The putrid smell of decayed organic material still lingers over drilling rigs today as the petroleum is freed from its rocky tomb. The origin of fossil fuels is certainly consistent with geologic processes that would have occurred during a global, catastrophic flood.

Since these resources may be considered non-renewable, then just as the need to replace coal with oil resulted in world wars, so should declining oil resources and production result in future wars. The global economy is now on the precipice of declining oil production and the prospect of world war is much closer than many realize. The regional, economic, and cyber wars occurring today are likely just the precursors of greater conflict to come.

During my career in the petroleum industry, I saw the data indicating that globally declining oil production is now rapidly approaching. Without new places to drill wells and find additional oil resources, production may level off for a time, but must decline eventually. The new wells being drilled today often have a more rapid oil production decline than past wells. To maintain overall production, the number of new wells being drilled has to continue at an even higher rate, or the consequences will be an even more rapid decline in production overall.

The main responsibility of a geoscientist in the petroleum industry is to identify new places to drill wells and find additional resources. I worked the primary oil-producing regions in America from the Williston Basin near Canada, throughout the Rocky Mountains, and into the Permian Basin of Texas; America's top oil producing province. Over the course of my career, the number of places to drill for new oil resources was fast diminishing. Of the new places identified to drill, the resources there were overall less than before, and were ever more costly to obtain.

Oil does not come from underground caverns, but solid rock. The ability to obtain oil or gas from solid rock is dependent on two things: the ability of the rock to store it, and the ability for oil to flow through the rock to a well. The first is called porosity and may be likened to the holes in a sponge, or the empty space in a jar of marbles. One might think of the marbles as tiny grains of minerals within the rock as a whole, and the oil as trapped between these grains just as one might fill a jar of marbles with liquid. Of course, the larger the grains, and the more holes in the rock, the better it is at storing liquids. The second is the ability for liquids or gas to flow through a rock, which is called permeability.

For about sixty years after the world wars ended, the petroleum industry pursued the best rock from which it was easy and cheap to obtain oil: the rock which had high porosity and high permeability. With time, the high quality rock was drilled up and production was set to decline. To avoid the economic and political consequences of declining production, after the turn of the millennium, America entered into both direct and indirect conflict in the Middle East, bringing other western allied troops alongside.

At this time, the American petroleum industry also began implementing an older technology that would allow production of oil from increasingly lower permeability rock. This technology is called "frac'ing" because it is the process of fracturing—artificially creating paths in the rock—to increase its natural permeability. The existing permeability between the mineral grains and through natural fractures is enhanced by pumping water and sand into the well at high pressures to further crack the rock. The sand is then left behind to hold the fractures open. The technology for creating artificial fractures is not new; it was developed back in the 1960's.

This enhanced, artificial ability to flow oil from frac'ing allowed the industry to economically pursue ever poorer quality, lower permeability rock. Today however, it is just becoming too costly to continue drilling new wells at the same rate as before, as they barely pay for themselves anymore. Even locations to drill in lower quality rock are getting drilled up leaving few places to drill new wells. As wells age their production declines and, as the rate of drilling replacements slows, the overall amount of oil being produced will inevitably decline.

Many working in the industry hope that a new technology will be developed to replace frac'ing, but it is most likely a vain hope as no such technology is currently being developed. Even if a new technology could be conceived and implemented rapidly, there will always be the problem that fossil fuels are non-renewable and most of the places to access them have been already discovered and produced. Also, it is quite telling that the amount of money being spent on exploration, the conceptualization and discovery of new resources, has dwindled down to a trickle around the world. Spending less on exploration is an indication that the industry has looked everywhere, and new resources are simply not to be found.

The hope that certain alternative sources of energy will replace fossil fuels is also fantasy. Wind and solar forms of energy are simply too inefficient, require too much infrastructure, and cost too much to make them solutions for weaning humanity away from petroleum. The mining for the heavy metals used in batteries, the manufacturing of windmills and solar panels, or even their use, are very dangerous to the environment. Promoting these as alternatives is simply peddling propaganda in the vain hope of keeping humanity in ignorant bliss of the coming rapid decline in oil production that is so essential to the modern, comfortable lifestyle expected.

Global oil production has been leveling off the last few years and is beginning to decline in many countries. Soon, even the top three oil producing countries: America, Russia, and Saudi Arabia, may have to admit that their production is also falling. As oil production falls, the risk of all-out war rises. Oil is a globally traded commodity and with less lubricant for the global economy, worldwide wars should be expected soon. The greedy desire of humanity to control declining resources may be the catalyst that opens the second seal for the red horse and its rider to emerge. The sword that this rider wields is the power to take peace from the earth and to bring a far greater genocide than ever experienced before.

When He opened the second seal, I heard the second living creature saying, "Come and see." Another horse, fiery red, went out. And it was granted to the one who sat on it to take peace from the earth [ge], and that people should kill one another; and there was given to him a great sword.
Revelation 6:3-4

Famine, Pestilence, & Persecution
Chapter 6

All economies run on energy and economic growth is heavily dependent on discovering new resources, thus growing energy supplies. Cheap energy from fossil fuels has allowed humanity to become accustomed to a life of relative ease. As energy supplies dwindle, ever increasingly absurd levels of debt are taken on to maintain that expected lifestyle. Although still relatively cheap, energy has become much more expensive over the last few decades and the debt-based financial system fueled by this energy is nearing its breaking point. Due to the height to which this financial system has been built up, the rate of its collapse may be far more rapid and severe than any decline in production.

Because those in power want to keep their position, war is often used as a distraction for a population suffering financially. Already the scales of justice are woefully out of balance. Those in power, to whom the scales are tipped favorably, will likely attempt to direct the resentment of the riotous mob outward instead of waiting for the justifiable anger to be directed upwards towards themselves. While economic turmoil leads to war, the consequences of war are far more severe. Victors may profit from war, but overall the destruction and death is far more costly. Lives lost results in further economic disaster, whether directly lost in battle, or indirectly through famine and pestilence.

The oil that is used to power tanks, planes, and ships should be used instead to power tractors and transport food to people. The fields are mined or burned, further reducing agricultural productivity; unnecessarily causing or exacerbating famines. Industry and other aspects of the economy are further casualties of war. As history shows, the damage from war continues long after the fighting stops and may even result in renewed war. After World War I, the Germans were forced into paying excessive war reparations. This was a burden their economy could not bear and directly resulted in an economic depression and great suffering among the German people. World War II was partly a rebellion against this economic oppression inflicted by the allied victors.

Today, the global economy struggles under a colossal mountain of debt from financing continual warfare in protracted conflicts like Afghanistan, Iraq, and Syria. Though America took the lead in these conflicts, it is not only the American people who bear their economic cost. Around the world suffering has increased due to the integration of the global economy which has been based on the dollar and backed by petroleum resources since the 1970's. Declining oil production and the burden of paying for previously endless wars are two factors that may open the third seal for the black horse rider to emerge, carrying scales upon which to weigh out an economic collapse more costly than ever before.

When He opened the third seal, I heard the third living creature say, "Come and see." So I looked, and behold, a black horse, and he who sat on it had a pair of scales in his hand. And I heard a voice in the midst of the four living creatures saying, "A quart [choinix] of wheat for a denarius, and three quarts [choinix] of barley for a denarius; and do not harm the oil and the wine." Revelation 6:4-5

The red and black horses run close together. Wars and economic distresses have always been companions from the time that wickedness entered the world. And yet, it is relatively simple to know if these two horsemen of Revelation have already rode forth or have yet to ride. The prophecy gives us an easily investigated ratio for the cost of wheat to silver. The Greek measurement of a [Χοῖνιξ] *choinix* is roughly equivalent to a quart and is defined by the amount of wheat necessary to sustain a grown man for a day. When this ratio was given, the denarius was the standard days wage and contained about 3.2 grams of silver. It is a rather simple process to look up the cost of these commodities and compare them using a mathematical conversion. Darkening clouds of economic turmoil may be seen on the horizon and yet the cost of wheat is nowhere near as high as predicted, nor even what it has been in recent history. Even while on-going wars, like the one in Ukraine, causes the price of wheat to rise and is a topic of global concern, the ratio is currently around ten *choinix* per denarius. That is ten days worth of food for one days labor.

In a global sense, humanity has always had the ability to provide itself clothing, homes, and other basic needs in addition to daily food. In the past, families had to work very hard, together making and growing necessities by hand. Life was difficult and with few comforts. Today, fossil fuels provide the energy and machines do the tasks necessary for manufacturing and agriculture. Many people have multiple sets of clothes and rooms in their homes. Even the poorest have televisions and cell phones. Life, despite the economic uncertainty, is still far more comfortable that it was even a century ago. Compared to history, the energy required to run the economy and provide basic needs, and also many luxuries, is still relatively cheap.

Instead of being grateful that today's living conditions are far above normal, greed prevails. Humanity no longer knows the how to work hard and as resources inevitably become more scarce, it will eventually require a full days work just to feed one person. Instead of returning to history's simple, hardworking lifestyle, the wicked march off to war to steal resources from others in the vain attempt to maintain what they have become accustomed too. A famine unlike anything the world has ever seen will certainly follow.

The righteous however, who have emulated the mercy of the Creator, who have not oppressed others, will find Him to be their defense amidst the war and their provider through the economic turmoil leading to severe famine. What is promised is not wealth and excess, but the basic necessities needed to sustain life.

…he who despises the gain of oppressions… his place of defense will be the fortress of rocks; bread will be given him, his water will be sure.
Isaiah 33:15-16

Unlike the riders of the red and black horses, it is not recorded what the rider of the fourth horse is holding, only that his name is Death. There are clues however, into how this rider destroys lives. The color of this horse in Greek is [χλωρός] *chloros*: a pale or sickly green color. Chlorophyll, a combination word with the Greek for leaf, is the chemical pigment that gives leaves a greenish color. However this rider kills, the scriptures state that he is working together with the other two horsemen to kill one quarter of the earth's population.

When He opened the fourth seal, I heard the voice of the fourth living creature saying, "Come and see." So I looked, and behold, a pale [chloros] horse. And the name of him who sat on it was Death, and Hades followed with him. And power was given to them over a fourth of the earth [ge], to kill with sword, with hunger, with death, and by the beasts of the earth [ge]. Revelation 6:7-8

Often with war, pestilence inevitably follows. In recent memory, the Spanish Flu, a deadly strain of influenza, began during World War I. It is estimated to have killed at least as many, to possibly even double the number of those who died fighting. One of the most likely reasons this pestilence is thought to have been so deadly is because of the insufficient nutrition and lack of available food during the war which lowered immune system resilience.

Today, the potential for pestilence associated with war may be even higher given the development of biological weapons. This extreme wickedness is yet another reason to believe that these horsemen may represent self-inflicted consequences and not the vengeful punishments of an angry deity. The first bowl plague also speaks of pestilence and it is possible this fourth horseman and this plague may be related and have relatively similar timing.

So the first went and poured out his bowl upon the earth [ge], and a foul and loathsome sore came upon the men who had the mark of the beast and those who worshiped his image. Revelation 16:2

This particular plague is poured out on the wicked, who follow the beast, not on the righteous. Thus there is hope of escape for the righteous from the natural consequences of human choice inflicted by the riders. Also, it should be obvious that those who follow the teachings of Yeshua, to love even their enemies, will not comprise the armies killed by the sword of the red horse rider.

Anyone who has not memorized Psalm 91 should consider doing so as it will be a source of great comfort and encouragement when these seals are soon opened. It speaks of protection for the righteous while thousands are dying in the war and pestilence around them.

You shall not be afraid of the terror by night, nor of the arrow that flies by day, nor of the pestilence that walks in darkness, nor of the destruction that lays waste at noonday. A thousand may fall at your side, and ten thousand at your right hand; but it shall not come near you. Only with your eyes shall you look, and see the reward of the wicked. Psalm 91:5-8

When the fifth seal is opened however, we see that the wicked have finally turned against the righteous, killing some. The statement that there is a certain number killed, indicates that the Creator has set a limit, known only to Him, and that many will be spared death by His mercy. Also, the assurance is given that this persecution will only be permitted for "*a little while*". Time and again throughout history, when difficult times arise, the wicked persecute and kill those who submit to keeping the Creator's laws of love. Because the righteous are protected and provided for, the envy of the wicked is aroused, but not their repentance.

When He opened the fifth seal, I saw under the altar the souls of those who had been slain for the word of God and for the testimony which they held…. and it was said to them that they should rest a little while longer, until both the number of their fellow servants and their brethren, who would be killed as they were, was completed. Revelation 6:9

Seals two through five may thus be thought of as natural, self-inflicted consequences of humanity's greed and hatred. It is human nature to seek ways to reduce the amount of effort necessary to generate the necessities and comforts desired. The use of fossil fuels to provide energy for everything from manufacturing, to agriculture, to transportation, has allowed humanity to attain a level of peace, comfort, and luxury in life that is historically unprecedented.

As little as a few hundred years ago, even kings in their majestic palaces did not travel as extensively, nor did they have access to the foods from around the world, the variety of conveniences, nor medical care choices that many enjoy today. As the ability to find new fossil fuel resources declines, humanity will not easily give up the benefits that are derived from their use. The selfishness of the wicked leads to stealing resources from others that they cannot, or will not, obtain by working harder for themselves. This wickedness may be responsible for the final chain reaction of war, famine, pestilence, and persecution, all resulting in widespread death, just as predicted by the seals of Revelation.

The wicked will kill each other as these first horsemen ride; one quarter of the earth's population will die. When the fifth seal is opened, there is a short time in which some of the righteous are also killed. However, this is a short time because Yeshua the Messiah returns at the opening of the very next seal to rescue his followers. The Creator, in His great mercy, will not allow such wickedness to finally destroy all humanity.

Horsemen Reduce Overpopulation
Chapter 7

It is recorded that the number who are killed by these horsemen is one quarter of humanity. Later, in Revelation 9 an entire army of two-hundred million additional horsemen kill a further third of humanity. These are a very large numbers, however, this death is the consequence of human choice, and not due to the supposed wrath of the Creator. Such a massive death toll is the exact opposite of what the Creator has desired for nearly six thousand years when He commanded the first pair to "*Be fruitful and multiply, and fill the earth*" in Genesis 1:28.

Now the number of the army of the horsemen was two hundred million; I heard the number of them…. By these three a third of mankind was killed—by the fire and the smoke and the brimstone which came out of their mouths. Revelation 9:16 & 18

Taking the present population of earth, which is estimated at just over eight billion people, and reducing the population by a quarter, results in the population being reduced to six billion by the first horsemen. Reducing this number by another third then results in a remainder of only four billion. Thus half of the present population is ultimately killed by horsemen.

A common narrative being promoted today by some in the scientific community, as well as many politicians and the global elite, is that the earth is overpopulated. Some of these appear to be actively seeking ways to reduce the human population by far more than the half predicted in Revelation. The number of deaths predicted in scripture is quite tame compared to the stated goals of some of those holding to an agenda of radical population reduction.

What the propaganda is not telling you, is that the earth is only overpopulated for a planet with no fossil fuel resources. After working in the petroleum industry, I taught high school environmental science in Amman, Jordan. One of the topics covered was population dynamics, which includes the concept of carrying capacity. Carrying capacity is the population any given ecosystem supports with the resources it contains. Naturally, if the resources available are increased, the carrying capacity of an ecosystem may simultaneously be increased. Overpopulation only occurs when the carrying capacity is surpassed. Population collapse then happens naturally as the ecosystem finds balance.

A common example taught in school is the population growth of reindeer on St. Matthew's Island, Alaska. There were no reindeer living on the island when they were introduced in 1944. Lichen was plentiful for them to eat in winter, and with no natural predators, the population quickly expanded. Eventually, the reindeer consumed all the lichen resources and over the winter of 1963 most starved as the population dropped precipitously from over six thousand individuals to less than fifty. For the first few reindeer, the amount of lichen was essentially limitless, they could eat as much as they wanted. At some point, the number of reindeer and the lichen reached a balance where the amount of new lichen growth was able to sustain the herd. This point was the carrying capacity for that island's ecosystem. Carrying capacity is a limit, the limiting factor being the lichen. The reindeer however, continued to eat the lichen as if it was limitless. Competition for lichen increased and the average weight of the reindeer began to drop even as the population continued to rise. This is overpopulation and it is unsustainable.

Now imagine that additional food was brought in for the reindeer. This would artificially raise the naturally limited carrying capacity of the island. A higher carrying capacity indicates increased access to resources and results in maintaining population balance, not overpopulation. The same is true for humanity. The earth today would be dangerously overpopulated if the carrying capacity of the planet had not been raised with the introduction of fossil fuel use.

Before the 1920's, the population of the earth was pretty well capped at around two billion people. This is likely the carrying capacity for the planet without the use of fossil fuels. Oil, the production of which began in earnest in the 1920's, raised the carrying capacity of the planet by making additional resources available to humanity. With oil to power tractors and other farm equipment, suddenly more new ground could be cultivated that could not have been previously. Along with the oil came natural gas, which is a primary component used in the creation of most fertilizers. In addition to more ground being plowed and planted, that ground could also be made more productive with these fertilizers. This period in time was called the Green Revolution as agricultural production expanded tremendously. Due to oil and gas, the carrying capacity of the planet was raised significantly, but only for a time.

Today, the earth is not overpopulated for the petroleum resources that it has. It would only be overpopulated should a surprise decrease occur in these available resources, thus lowering the carrying capacity. Those who promote the idea that the earth is overpopulated are not being fully transparent. Only falling petroleum production would result in a falling carrying capacity. What most are not being told is that production will soon begin to decline because even the poor quality rock has now been mostly drilled up and the number of additional places to drill new wells is already dropping off significantly. The coming rapid drop in production is the reason for pushing the concept of overpopulation and the supposed solution of population reduction. The key, limiting resource to growing enough food and transporting it to the consumers is petroleum. The earth's current carrying capacity is based on petroleum and the earth cannot sustain its current population without it.

What the red horse rider of Revelation is showing us is that those who hold power will not wait for the population to decline naturally as less food is available and starvation ensues. To do so would be to risk loosing their power in the inevitable riots that would follow. In fact, this scenario is exactly what happened during the Arab Spring in 2011 as riots over higher food prices, especially wheat, toppled many governments. In their lust for power, even so-called democratic regimes will go to war in a vain attempt to steal and control as much resources as they can take by force. But war is destructive and will only result in speeding the process of population collapse by using these resources up more rapidly than in times of peace or by destroying needed resources and killing people outright.

While the target goal of some who promote population reduction is to reduce the population to around one billion, or one eighth of the current population, the horsemen tell us that the Creator puts the insanity to an end, after only half are killed, by sending Yeshua to rescue those who follow His laws of love. I cannot emphasize enough how much the mercy of the Creator is demonstrated in the entirety of the book of Revelation. It is a theme I will return to over and over again in this book. When one looks at the seals of Revelation as primarily natural consequences of humanity's greed and hatred, then one may see that our Creator is truly merciful to allow a period of tribulation in hopes of bringing humanity to repentance. The extreme wickedness must eventually be brought to an end however. The reduction of the population will never be allowed to progress to the goal, but will be stopped short.

Not long after the wicked begin to persecute and kill the righteous, the sixth seal is opened and Yeshua returns. The wicked cannot stand to see their plans thwarted and instead of choosing life, repentance, and rescue, they ultimately choose to destroy themselves. When one carefully reads the sixth seal, one may see that the final destruction of the wicked is their own choice. Note the order of the events presented after the sixth seal is opened. There is a great earthquake, the mountains are moving from their place, and then the wicked are attempting to hide in them. They are so determined to get away from love and mercy that they instead run towards collapsing mountains, choosing to be destroyed rather than rescued. They fail to repent and discern the love and mercy provided for their rescue and instead are commanding the mountains to collapse upon themselves.

> *...every mountain and island was moved out of its place. And the kings of the earth [ge], the great men, the rich men, the commanders, the mighty men, every slave and every free man, hid themselves in the caves and in the rocks of the mountains, and said to the mountains and rocks, "Fall on us and hide us from the face of Him who sits on the throne and from the wrath of the Lamb!" Revelation 6:14-16*

From the opening of second seal, right through the events following the opening of the sixth seal, the wicked are consistently choosing death instead of life. Their selfish greed, lust for power, baseless hatred, and intolerance of others lead to increasingly difficult consequences. From the time the red horse rider picks up the sword, those who choose to live by the sword must also eventually die by the sword.

...he who kills with the sword must be killed with the sword. Revelation 13:10

But Yeshua said to him, "Put your sword in its place, for all who take the sword will perish by the sword." Matthew 26:52

Yeshua told his follower Peter to put away his sword because the great conflict between good and evil is not fought with violence. It is not by a physical sword that the remaining wicked finally perish, they are killed trying to hide from the word of truth.

Now I saw heaven opened, and behold, a white horse. And he who sat on him was called Faithful and True... and his name is called The Word of God... Now out of His mouth goes a sharp sword... Revelation 19:11, 13, & 15

The final horse rider in Revelation is Yeshua who rides a white horse when he returns. Instead of carrying a bow while riding the white horse when the first seal is opened in Revelation 6:1-2, here he is portrayed as having a sword coming "*out of his mouth*" representing the fact that he is "*The Word of God*". This sword-in-mouth motif spans Revelation from the beginning to the end (Revelation 1:16, 2:12 & 16, 19:15 & 21) and points to who is the ultimate victor: Yeshua the Messiah, the Word of the Creator.

The sword that proceeds from his mouth is not a physical sword, wielded for the destruction of the wicked. They have died calling for the mountains to fall on themselves. This is a sword of mercy, the one designed to surgically remove stony hearts so that a new heart may be given. As the scriptures of truth are read *tamiyd*, they point us back to our merciful Creator. These scriptures guide us down the straight path, the path of love that was first trod by Yeshua the Messiah, our example.

I will give you a new heart and put a new spirit within you; I will take the heart of stone out of your flesh and give you a heart of flesh. Ezekiel 36:26

TRUMPETS & BOWLS AS GEOLOGIC SIGNS
Section III

Yea, though I walk through the
valley of the shadow of death,
I will fear no evil; for You are with me;
Your rod and Your staff, they comfort me.
You prepare a table before me
in the presence of my enemies;
You anoint my head with oil;
my cup runs over.
Surely goodness and mercy
shall follow me all the days of my life;
and I will dwell in the house
of YHWH forever.

Psalm 23:4-6

The Falling Star Given the Key
Chapter 8

Recorded right after the seals, in Revelation 8:2-16:21, are the trumpet warnings and the pouring out of the bowls containing the final plagues. The previous section discussed the decline of producible geologic resources and the natural consequences of humanity's choices. This section will investigate the hypothesis that most of the trumpet and bowls will be fulfilled by a sequence of geologic catastrophes initiated due to a single root cause. As already discussed briefly, this cause may be a celestial event or object.

Celestial objects striking the earth are directly mentioned in several of the trumpets. Other signs of the trumpets and bowls mention darkness, smoke, fire, and great heat which may be related. The geology associated with these signs and the possibility they are likely all linked to the same root cause will be discussed, each in more detail, in the subsequent chapters.

One possible mechanism by which all of these signs may be linked is an adjustment to the earth's orbit to be closer to the sun. This adjustment might be caused by either some kind of celestial event or a massive object gravitationally pulling the earth closer. This object, probably an asteroid, is not mentioned directly in prophecy. Such an object may be unveiled by understanding the many additional prophecies that point to its existence as their cause.

The scriptures contain many prophecies that may describe asteroids such as Daniel's recounting of King Nebuchadnezzar's forgotten dream. In this dream the stone may be an asteroid since they are made of rock while comets are made of ice.

You watched while a stone was cut out without hands, which struck the image on its feet of iron and clay, and broke them in pieces. Daniel 2:34

It is entirely possible to interpret this prophecy both literally, as an asteroid, and spiritually. Yeshua compares himself to the *"chief cornerstone"* as recorded in Matthew 21:42. As such, Yeshua is the ultimate victor, breaking in pieces the world empires portrayed by the image in this dream. Although he does not speak of direct impacts, Yeshua may have still had this stone in mind when later that very day he spoke of *"men's hearts failing them from fear and the expectation of those things which are coming on the earth"* as discussed in chapter four.

In the trumpet warnings of Revelation 8-11, there are three direct impacts of celestial objects mentioned that impact the earth and are described as: a *"great mountain burning with fire"*, *"a great star falling from heaven, burning like a torch"*, and *"a star fallen from heaven to earth [ge]"*. These events all occur, respectively, with the blowing of the second, third, and fifth trumpet warnings. It is possible that these trumpets are warning humanity of a series of celestial objects colliding with earth much like what happened to Jupiter in July of 1994. I still remember vividly the great excitement around the world when comet Shoemaker-Levy 9 created multiple impact sites across the planet which were visible from earth as as band of black spots. The largest of these spots was almost equal to the diameter of the earth itself!

The comet had previously broken up into a chain of smaller comets, the largest still being two kilometers in diameter. Over the course of six days, each piece successively and spectacularly impacted Jupiter. The fireballs associated with the comets entering the atmosphere reached a burning hot 23,700°C. Revelation describes these falling stars as great, burning mountains; a description that is very appropriate. Not only did these comets fit the description, they also demonstrated the possibility of a series of impacts occurring in rapid succession. Many small fireballs are constantly burning up in earth's atmosphere. The number of sightings has risen significantly in the past few years just like the number of earthquakes. This increase might just be warnings of the big one, or big ones, that are yet to come.

The second trumpet gives the location of the first impact as the sea and the result is that a third of the sea creatures die. Many would die as a direct result of the impact, while their dead bodies would result in a bacterial bloom just like what occurred during the global flood. Bacterial blooms today sometimes result in red tide events that suffocate and kill sea creatures. The sea becoming "*blood*" could be a description of the color and smell of a red tide and not that the sea actually turns to blood.

Then the second angel sounded: and something like a great mountain burning with fire was thrown into the sea, and a third of the sea became blood. And a third of the living creatures in the sea died, and a third of the ships were destroyed. Revelation 8:8-9

After second bowl plague is poured out, it is predicted that all the sea creatures eventually die when the entire sea turns to "*blood*". Obviously, a third of sea creatures cannot die after all of them die so this must happen sequentially after the second trumpet is blown. The second bowl can only happen after the second trumpet and not the other way around, thus establishing their timing relative to each other. The parallel second bowl plague is probably a continuation of the consequences of the impact in the sea mentioned in the second trumpet.

Then the second angel poured out his bowl on the sea, and it became blood as of a dead man; and every living creature in the sea died. Revelation 16:3

The towering tsunami resulting from such an impact in the sea would destroy many ships as also mentioned in the second trumpet. The earthquake-induced tsunamis in Indonesia in 2004 and Japan in 2011 would be of a much smaller scale, and yet still devastating demonstrations of the power of massive tsunamis to destroy ships.

For the day of YHWH of hosts shall come upon everything proud and lofty, …Upon all the ships of

Tarshish, and upon all the beautiful sloops... When
He arises to shake the earth mightily.
Isaiah 2:12, 16, & 19

The third trumpet gives the location of the second impact as on land. The result is that drinking water becomes bitter. A potential explanation for how the waters become bitter may be the release of pollution into fresh water sources due to fracturing of the earth's crust from an impact.

Then the third angel sounded: and a great star [aster] fell from heaven, burning like a torch, and it fell on a third of the rivers and on the springs of water. The name of the star [aster] is Wormwood. A third of the waters became wormwood, and many men died from the water, because it was made bitter. Revelation 8:10-11

The ability of pollution to get into drinking water through fractures is well established. In some places where there are gas fields, such as in Fort Lupton, Colorado, residents in the area have been able to light on fire the bubbles in the water coming from their faucets. In another gas field near Riverton, Wyoming, chemicals found in a few water wells were traced back to chemicals used in nearby agriculture. It was likely that in both instances, natural fractures were the main conduits by which these pollutants entered the drinking water. Because of the breaking up of the earth's crust during the global flood, natural fractures are pervasive. However, artificial fractures created by frac'ing may also have contributed to the overall ability to flow pollutants in these areas.

An impact would certainly create many more local fractures than industry frac'ing ever could. A large enough impact might also increase the number of earthquakes around the earth as stresses within the crust would be thrown out of balance. This would result in more natural fractures globally. With all of the pesticides, herbicides, mine tailings, industrial waste, and so forth; littering the whole earth at this point, there is extreme danger of widespread loss of containment for all this pollution and subsequent contamination of drinking water worldwide.

Just like the second trumpet is blown before the second bowl is poured out, here there is also a relative timing that may be determined. After the third trumpet sounds, only a third of the freshwater sources become bitter while after the third bowl is poured out, all of these waters turn to "*blood*". Bacteria might grow and replicate more rapidly in this polluted water, duplicating what may happen to the seas.

Then the third angel poured out his bowl on the rivers and springs of water, and they became blood.
Revelation 16:4

The fourth trumpet warning does not explicitly speak of another impact on earth. Rather, it speaks of the sun, moon, and stars being "*struck*". The Greek word from which the English word "*struck*" is translated has an uncertain derivation that is only used this one time in scripture. This makes it difficult to unravel the word's meaning based on its context in other verses.

Then the fourth angel sounded: and a third of the sun was struck, a third of the moon, and a third of the stars [aster], so that a third of them were darkened... Revelation 8:12

It may be that the focus of this verse should be on the darkening of these celestial luminaries, rather than on them being struck. To physically strike one third of the stars of heaven, which are almost limitless in number, is statistically nearly impossible. Rather, the appearance of a third being struck, from the standpoint of an earth-based observer seems more likely. A potential mechanism for darkening the skies and obscuring these luminaries would be a significant increase in volcanic activity. The result would be large volumes of ash, or *"smoke"* from the *"bottomless pit"* being ejected into the atmosphere. Increasing volcanic activity may itself be attributed to impacts, or even simply an orbital adjustment. Such indirect geologic consequences will be discussed further in chapter twelve. This chapter focuses on direct predictions of impacts and the consequences that are mentioned along with them.

The fifth trumpet appears to warn of a third celestial object falling to earth which also causes darkness, similarly to the fourth trumpet, and smoke. The Greek word [αὐτῷ] *auto* is a little ambiguous here and many translations state that *"he"*, meaning the angel, was given the key. However, some like the NASB® translates the word as "*it*", meaning that the star was given the key.

Then the fifth angel sounded: and I saw a star [aster] fallen from heaven to the earth [ge]. To him [auto] was given the key to the bottomless pit. And he opened the bottomless pit, and smoke arose out of the pit like the smoke of a great furnace. So the sun and the air were darkened because of the smoke of the pit. Revelation 9:1-2

One common assumption is that the angel is the star that fell from heaven and various symbolic or spiritual interpretations for this fallen angel have been proposed. However, there is also a more literal interpretation where these verses describe a natural event. Since none of the other angels with trumpets appear to be involved in any way in the events they warn about, the translations that state that it is the star that receives the key are likely more accurate. It is far simpler and more consistent to interpret this trumpet literally, thus fitting with the theme of direct impacts described by two of the previous trumpets.

This raises some intriguing possibilities for how these verses are to be understood. The star falling to earth may be the key event that unlocks, or causes, the biological and geological catastrophes discussed in this chapter. Asteroids impacting the earth may be the indirect cause of the poisoning of the seas and freshwater that kills all of the sea creatures, as well as the smoke arising from the bottomless pit that obscures the celestial luminaries. The concept that a large asteroid might be this key cause of further natural catastrophes, besides just impacts, is exactly the main hypothesis presented in this book. It is almost as if these two verses are implying this very hypothesis, but in prophetic language.

So far it has been shown that three out of the seven trumpets and two of the bowls may be directly related to impacts and that the two bowls are poured out soon after their respective trumpets are blown. Keep in mind that what are being proposed however, are only hypotheses attempting to explain how these prophecies may be describing literal occurrences in the physical, natural creation. There may be other hypotheses I have not considered for ways in which to physically fulfill these prophecies. There are also the symbolic or spiritual hypotheses that this book does not discuss.

Even though many of the warnings given may be explained with the root cause being a celestial event or object, the hypothesis does not necessarily explain all the warnings given. This chapter skipped hypothesizing an explanation for the first trumpet. Still, this warning appears to be describing events in the physical realm.

The first angel sounded: and hail and fire followed, mingled with blood, and they were thrown to the earth [ge]. And a third of the trees were burned up, and all green grass was burned up. Revelation 8:7

The hail, fire, and blood may describe small pieces falling to earth from an asteroid that passes nearby before the first one impacts. However, I am not satisfied with this explanation as the hail seems more weather-related or possibly related to an icy comet. While blood in the rivers and seas may be explained as a red tide, there is no good explanation for blood falling from heaven. The consequences of this warning are still geologic regardless of its cause however. Because trees and grass are burned up, the lack of vegetation would lead to increased runoff, soil erosion, and flooding.

While many various geologic events may be described in the scriptures, it seems that out of all of them, asteroids and their consequences would get the most attention and thus make an ideal way of proclaiming to humanity Yeshua the Messiah's soon return.

When I consider Your heavens, the work of Your fingers, the moon and the stars, which You have set in place; What is man that You think of him, and a son of man that You are concerned about him?
Psalm 8:3-4

Extreme Global Warming
Chapter 9

The trumpets and bowls discussed in the previous chapter are not the only signs that may be caused by celestial events or objects. The fourth and sixth bowls in Revelation 16 predict scorching fire, great heat, and the Euphrates River drying up. All of these things indicate natural global warming caused by an increase in the amount of energy from the sun hitting the earth, possibly because the orbit of the earth has shifted closer to the sun. If such an orbital adjustment were to occur, regardless of what caused it, the result would be heating from the sun that would immediately begin to warm the earth at a rate far greater than the rate of the hotly debated global warming that human activity is supposedly causing. The extreme heat that is being described in these verses is much more than the few degrees that is supposedly the consequence of humanity's lack of care for their environment.

Then the fourth angel poured out his bowl on the sun, and power was given to him [auto] to scorch men with fire. And men were scorched with great heat… Revelation 16:8-9

Just as in the warning of the fifth trumpet, the Greek word *auto* here is often translated as "*him*" instead of "*it*" as in the NASB®. This word should not be translated as referring to the angel giving the warning, instead, it is again referring to yet another celestial object. In this warning the word *auto* is referring to the sun that is being given the power to scorch men, just as in the fifth trumpet it was the star that was *"given the key to the bottomless pit."*

Then the sixth angel poured out his bowl on the great river Euphrates, and its water was dried up, so that the way of the kings from the east might be prepared. Revelation 16:12

It is possible to get dry riverbeds by re-routing rivers with an earthquake, but re-routing is not what the verse is talking about, it clearly states that the Euphrates River in Mesopotamia is dried up. There are two ways in which to dry up a river. One would be to increase the rate of evaporation of the water in the river. This may be accomplished in tandem with global warming as warmer water evaporates more quickly than cool water. Another way is to decrease the amount of rain falling within the river's catchment basin: the area that the river drains. Both increased evaporation and less rainfall are consequences of global warming and would actually work together to dry up the river. Should the earth be moved into an orbit closer to the sun, and thus experience extreme natural global warming, the result would be quite rapid and significant changes to weather patterns around the world.

The main driver of weather on earth are its oceans because they are the source of most of the water that is available to enter the atmosphere by evaporation and later fall elsewhere as precipitation.

Increasing the temperature of the oceans allows for more rapid evaporation of seawater. Warmer oceans result in far more precipitation: rain, hail, and oddly enough, even snow. With warming oceans due to extreme global warming, the frequency and severity of storms like hurricanes, tornados, and blizzards also increases significantly.

One major contributing factor for the past ice ages was the warm oceans immediately following the global flood. A significant amount of the water that caused the flood came from deep underground via "*the fountains of the great deep*" as described in Genesis 7:11. This water would have been very hot given its origin deep underground. After the rain stopped, these flood waters began to recede into the newly created ocean basins and dry land was once again exposed. The sun began to shine again and evaporation of this warmer water caused heavy precipitation in the first few centuries after the flood. The precipitation that fell at lower latitudes, as rain, caused significant erosion, while at higher latitudes, the precipitation fell as snow and accumulated as thick ice sheets around the poles. The melting and retreat of this ice has been going on for centuries and those that remain today are the finally vanishing reminders of the consequences of the flood. The slight global warming trend observed and debated today has actually been going on since the flood and is just a return towards pre-flood normal conditions.

Changing the temperature of the oceans not only changes how much evaporation occurs, leading to precipitation, but also where that precipitation falls. Because wind is driven by rising heat, more heat will result in changing the wind patterns. In the future then, it is entirely possible that the area that the Euphrates River drains would experience severe drought while other places would receive much more precipitation.

Then the sixth angel sounded: and I heard a voice from the four horns of the golden altar which is before God, saying to the sixth angel who had the trumpet, "Release the four angels who are bound at the great river Euphrates." So the four angels, who had been prepared for the hour and day and month and year, were released to kill a third of mankind.
Revelation 9:13-15

The sixth bowl and the sixth trumpet are likely parallel warnings as both speak of a crossing of the Euphrates River. The sixth trumpet does not mention the drying of the river, but it does imply that there is some impediment, probably water, that prevents an army of two-hundred million horsemen from being able to cross it. Because of the parallels in these verses it would also be logical to conclude that these signs have the same relative timing.

As discussed in the previous chapter, the second trumpet and bowl are parallel and the third trumpet and bowl are also parallel. In chapter twelve the fifth trumpet and bowl both describe darkness and it will be discussed how they are also parallel. At first glance however, the fourth trumpet and bowl seem like exact opposites. In the fourth trumpet the celestial luminaries are darkened while in the fourth bowl the sun scorches with great heat. Thus the fourth bowl appears parallel to the sixth trumpet and bowl with all three being due to extreme global warming. In contrast however, the fourth trumpet appears to parallel the fifth trumpet and bowl; all three of which describe darkness. In chapter twelve, this darkness is linked to volcanic ash suspended in the atmosphere and being spread out over the entire earth. This ash would not only result in a blanket of haze shading the earth, but, as it is composed of particles of volcanic glass, would also reflect some of the heat from the sun back into empty space. The result would be global cooling and not "*great heat*".

Volcanic ash has been the cause of global cooling in the past. 1816 is often described as the year without a summer, as cooler temperatures were particularly noticeable in Europe and parts of North America. The cause of this cooling was the largest volcanic eruption ever recorded the previous spring. In April of 1815 Mount Tambora had violently ejected an estimated 38-51 cubic miles of ash into the atmosphere in far away Indonesia. The fine particles of ash suspended in the atmosphere and spread out over the entire earth reflecting some of the heat from the sun back into empty space.

The conundrum of how the fourth trumpet and bowl might also be parallel signs, just like the others, is resolved when it is determined that both the celestial luminaries being darkened and the sun scorching with "*great heat*" may have the same root cause. If the earth were to move into an orbit closer to the sun, extreme global warming would result. Such warming would not only warm the atmosphere, but also the crust of the earth. Warming of the crust would lead to increased volcanic activity as will be discussed more fully in future chapters. Increasing volcanic activity creating thick clouds of ash would darken the celestial luminaries. While ash in the atmosphere could cause some global cooling, the earth being closer to the sun would, at the same time, cause far greater global warming.

John's juxtaposing of the "*sun scorching men with great heat*" in the fourth bowl with the darkening of the celestial luminaries in the fourth trumpet may be a way of subtly drawing attention to the Creator's mercy. This juxtaposition is placed in the middle of the trumpets and bowls. While the wicked are being scorched with extreme heat, the ash may provide shade in places so that there is some relief for the righteous. Only a merciful Creator would so arrange the final warnings in such a way that while one, the scorching heat, would end humanity, the other, the darkness, is a blessing in disguise sent to allow humanity time to consider these warnings and turn towards the Creator as their source of life.

Be merciful to me, O God, be merciful to me! For my soul trusts in You; and in the shadow of Your wings I will make my refuge, until these calamities have passed by. Psalm 57:1

YHWH is your keeper; YHWH is your shade at your right hand. The sun shall not strike you by day…
Psalm 121:5-6

Raash of Heaven & Mot of Earth
Chapter 10

Before continuing to investigate the warnings in Revelation, the next couple of chapters will turn attention to older prophetic scriptures. Some verses from the Hebrew scriptures, when considered literal, also speak of geologic events. This chapter will take a deep dive into those verses that describe the earth shaking. Curiously, some even describe the heavens being shaken as well. Might such verses refer not only to earthquakes, but also to shifting of the earth's orbit?

First, let us look at the Hebrew word [מִמְּקוֹמָהּ] *mimmeqowmah* which means: out of its usual place or position. While the root of the word is found in many places, there are only two verses where this specific word is spelled this way. These verses state that the earth itself will move out of its "*place*", or position, and that this event will occur when the heavens themselves are [רגז] *ragaz,* which means to shake, quake, tremble, move, or be disturbed.

He shakes [ragaz] the earth out of its place [mimmeqowmah], and its pillars tremble. Job 9:6

Therefore I will shake [ragaz] the heavens, and the earth will move [raash] out of her place [mimmeqowmah] in the wrath of YHWH of hosts and in the day of His fierce anger. Isaiah 13:13

Another adjective used by Isaiah to describe how the earth moves is [רעש] *raash*, and it is a fascinating, multi-faceted word whose most ancient recorded usage is in Job, and yet it is still used to describe earthquakes in modern Hebrew. While investigating this word, I found it contains emotions of trembling in fear as well as sudden or violent movement. In speaking to Job, the Creator uses this word to convey contrasts between a fearless war horse and a startled locust.

"Do you make him leap [raash] like locusts?
His majestic snorting is frightening… He races over
the ground with a roar [raash] and fury…"
Job 39:20 & 24

Above, I chose to use the NASB® translation, but also allow me to also propose my own expanded paraphrase that I hope may convey a little more of the richness and depth of the Hebrew, which never ceases to amaze me. This one word speaks to our emotions as well as our visual and auditory senses. Imagine you are standing in the path of a charging war horse, in fear and trembling as if you were the locust, feeling the earth tremble under its pounding hooves, just like during an earthquake.

Can you startle the war horse like a locust or make him jump away in fright? No! Instead his majestic snorting strikes terror, it is not like the sound of a locust rustling in flight. With rage he leaps over the ground, devouring the distance. He does not tremble in fear, instead he causes the earth to rattle.

As a geoscientist, my attention is not drawn to the startling cause of the movement, nor to the resulting sounds: either of a locust's wings rustling or of things rattling in an earthquake. The facet of how the word describes movement is what catches my eyes. *Raash* describes sudden movement such as when a locust is startled and then suddenly moves, leaping from one place to another. The earth also experiences similar jarring movements during an earthquake. In scripture however, it is not just the earth that experiences this sudden movement, but the heavens also according to the prophets Joel and Haggai. But how is it that the heavens move and is there any similarity with how a locust leaps suddenly from one place to another?

The earth quakes [ragaz] before them, the heavens tremble [raash]… the heavens and earth will shake [raash]… Joel 2:10 & 3:16

For thus says YHWH of hosts: "Once more (it is a little while) I will shake [raash] heaven and earth, the sea and dry land…" Haggai 2:6

The Hebrew language is rich in words related to shaking and there are more to discuss before returning to the question of the heaven's shaking. The richness of Hebrew on this topic should not be surprising given that the land of the prophets: the Levant—where these scriptures were recorded and preserved—is located along active faults where earthquakes were, and are commonly experienced. Another word is [טומ] *mot* meaning to tremble or slip.

David uses this word to describe both earthquakes and the slipping of a foot while walking.

Uphold my steps in Your paths, that my footsteps may not slip [mot]. Psalm 17:5

You have made the earth tremble [raash]; You have broken it; heal its breaches, for it is shaking [mot]. Psalm 60:2

As a geoscientist, I find that using a word that describes the slipping of a foot is a very appropriate word to use for the way blocks of land slip along a fault. I have often demonstrated how the various types of faults, described in chapter three, move by using my hands in a similar slipping motion. Recall also that a slipping movement along faults is the cause of many mountains being created in the first place. As discussed, many mountains were created during the global flood to raise the continents above the ocean basins and drain off the flood waters.

At first, these mountains rose because of a horizontal maximum compressive stress. Afterwards, some, like the ones I studied in central Wyoming, then began to collapse under their own weight as the maximum compressive stress shifted to vertical. The direction of movement along faults underlying these mountains reversed as an extensional stress regime prevailed and the mountains began to slip back towards the sea.

This observation is not limited to only science, scripture also records both the historical collapse of mountains and also predicts their eventual complete collapse into the sea. This future slip and collapse will be discussed more fully in the next chapter.

Scripture is clear however, that it is more than just mountains that slip similarly to a foot. The earth itself will slip when its *"foundations"* will be shaken. These verses point towards an event that affects the earth as a whole, and is much more geologically significant than just an earthquake. It is possible that the earth, slipping from its *"foundations"* means that it will slip from its orbit, into another orbit, just as mountains slip along faults, or a foot slips across the ground.

...they walk about in darkness; all the foundations of the earth are unstable [raash]. Psalm 82:5

...the foundations [mowcadah] of the earth are shaken [raash]. The earth is violently broken, the earth is split open, the earth is shaken exceedingly [mot mot] . Isaiah 24:18-19

The double use of the word *mot* emphasizes an utterly complete motion. The words *raash* and *mot* are found together here, indicating that the motion being described is that of the earth moving suddenly from its position, just like as a leaping grasshopper or slipping foot. The word *"foundations"* is translated in a few verses from the word [מוסדה] *mowcadah*, which may mean stone foundations, as in Jeremiah 51:26, but which does not usually refer to something physical like stone. For example, in Isaiah 58:12, the word is used in referring to the *"foundations [mowcadah] of many generations..."*

The lack of physical foundations for the earth is noted from ancient times by Job who states that the earth is hung on nothing. Further, the Creator, the highest authority, states that the foundations of the earth are not something that may be found, implying that they cannot be physical.

He stretches out the north over empty space; He hangs the earth on nothing. Job 26:7

Thus says YHWH: "If heaven above can be measured, and the foundations [mowcadah] of the earth searched out beneath…" Jeremiah 31:37

It would seem rather confusing then that the earth's foundations, which do not exist in a physical sense, are being shaken and moved like a leaping grasshopper or slipping foot. If there are no tangible foundations on which the earth rests, then what is beneath it, holding it in its position? The simple answer is that it is the invisible force of gravity that holds the earth in its "*place*". It is the gravitational pull of the sun that keeps the earth spinning in its orbit around the sun. What would happen then if the mass, and thus the gravity of the sun increased, or a new celestial source of gravity, such as a large asteroid, would pass near enough to earth to pull on it? Might the earth slip out of its orbit?

The answer is theoretically yes, if the passing asteroid was close enough and had enough mass. A passing asteroid would be a temporary event as it would exert a gravitational pull for only a short time before the dominant pull of the sun would resume.

Before the asteroid passed, the earth would be in its present orbit, then it might rapidly move while the asteroid passed, and finally it might settle into a new orbit after the gravity of the asteroid stopped pulling on it. Whatever the cause, the change in orbit would not be instantaneous, but it would be sudden, much like the leap of a grasshopper. In doing so, the earth would slip along the gravitational fabric of space much like blocks of land move along a fault or a foot slips. A geoscientist might even describe such an event using these very words.

The gravitational fabric of space might be explained as similar to a giant sheet on which the celestial orbs sit like balls. Picture then, a ball being rolled close by another. Due to the way the balls bend down the sheet around themselves, if another ball were to pass nearby, the two balls would slip along the sheet toward each together, much like gravity pulls together passing celestial orbs. Both of the words: *raash* and *mot*, imply a similar rapid, linear movement from one place to another. This is exactly what would happen if the earth were to slip into a new orbit along gravity's fabric.

There are Hebrew words used in the context of earthquakes that do not indicate a sudden, linear movement. Instead, they describe a back and forth motion like the waves of the sea or the trembling of a leaf. They are very appropriate words to use to describe the way the ground moves back and forth during an earthquake. It should be noted however, that these particular words are seldom used and do not appear in the context of the foundations of the earth, nor in describing the time of the end. One is the word [געש] *gaash*, which means to shake, surge, or toss "*to and fro*" like waves on the sea as in Jeremiah 5:22. Another word is [ערץ] *arats* which means to tremble, dread, or shock. It is used in Job 13:25 to refer to the trembling of a leaf. It may be used also for emotional dread and the physical manifestation of that dread in the form of trembling. In the examples below that do refer to earthquakes, there is no mention of the heavens, nor of the foundations of the earth.

Then the earth shook [gaash] and trembled [raash]; the foundations of the hills also quaked [ragaz] and were shaken [gaash], because He was angry.
Psalm 18:7

They shall go into the holes of the rocks, and into the caves of the earth, from the terror of YHWH and the glory of His majesty, when He arises to shake [arats] the earth mightily. Isaiah 2:19

It would be natural to conclude that these and similar verses are simply talking about nothing more than earthquakes. The Hebrew words *raash* and *ragaz* are also used in Psalm 18 which indicates that these words may also be used to also describe mere earthquakes. It is very important to look at these words in context, especially in the verses referring to the time of the end where these words are applied to the foundations of the earth and also the heavens. In those contexts, the words must then be describing something more than just a common earthquake.

In Isaiah 13 and 24, shown before, the NKJV® translates *ragaz*, *raash*, and *mot* each as "*shake*". Translating all three Hebrew words using a single English word results in a loss of understanding what these verses are trying to tell us. Below, the verses are repeated using different English words that were chosen based on investigating how these Hebrew words were used in various contexts throughout the scriptures.

Therefore I will disturb *[ragaz] the heavens…*

…the foundations of the earth leap *[raash]. The earth is violently broken, the earth is split open, the earth* slips completely *[mot mot].*

The earth leaping or slipping completely out of its usual position sounds a lot like an orbital shift to this geoscientist. Because these verses, and the others like them, also speak of the heavens being disturbed, it is much more probable that they are speaking about an astronomical event and not just an earthquake. From the standpoint of an earth-based observer, the heavens would appear to be disturbed, suddenly leaping into a new position, slipping along the fabric of gravity as the position of the earth relative to all the celestial luminaries would have changed.

It would not even require modern astronomical instruments to know this change was happening as it would be shown by simple sundials. Afterwards, the lengths of years and months would likely also change. With such simple observations to make, the

Creator, in His great mercy, has ensured that one day soon, all humanity will know for sure that these prophecies have been fulfilled and that He has power over creation. Even if somehow, some missed seeing the celestial event or object, an unmistakable change in the length of years and months would ensure adequate warning to spiritually prepare for the soon coming rescue that would necessarily follow such a catastrophe.

Surely the Lord YHWH does nothing, unless He reveals His secret to His servants the prophets.
Amos 3:7

Casting Mountains Into the Sea
Chapter 11

Astronomical events are certainly predicted in the heavens, and yet there are also subtle clues of related geologic events on earth. Each of the verses below are very adamant that more than just a few rocks are affected and that the earth itself is entirely broken and fractured. Multiple Hebrew words are used such as [פרר] *parar*, which means to break or divide; [פצם] *patsam*, meaning to split open; and [שבר] *sheber*, defined as breaking or fracturing. The phenomenal power over these geologic processes is attributed to the Creator by David.

The earth is violently broken, the earth is split open [parar parar], the earth is shaken exceedingly [mot mot]. Isaiah 24:19

You have made the earth tremble [raash]; You have broken it [patsam]; heal its breaches [sheber], for it is shaking [mot]. Psalm 60:2

Extensional stress regimes in the earth's crust are the cause of this breaking, splitting, or fracturing. As the crust is being extended, blocks of land are moving away from each other rather than together. The crust is no longer being compressed together causing mountains to rise higher. Instead, mountains are undergoing extension and collapsing. They are slipping along underlying faults, disappearing as if sliding back into the sea.

Therefore we will not fear, even though the earth be removed, and though the mountains be carried [mot] into the midst of the sea... Psalm 46:2

Job speaks more than once of this geologic process. He states that the Creator "*removes*" the mountains, translated from [עתק] *atheq*, which may also mean to move away, thus implying extension. The NKJV® translation also states that the Creator "*overturns*" the mountains, but this is not an accurate translation. A better translation of the Hebrew here would be that the Creator overthrows the mountains. The same word is used to describe the destruction of Sodom and Gomorrah in Genesis 19. These cities were not turned upside down, but were overthrown or destroyed.

He removes [atheq] the mountains, and they do not know when He overturns them in His anger. Job 9:6

Another verse, also found in Job, may likewise indicate the collapse of mountains. In the thesis for my Master of Science degree, I used the NASB® translation of the verse below because it appears to be describing similar observations to those I made of the fracturing and partial collapse of mountains in central Wyoming.

*But the falling mountain crumbles away,
And the rock moves from its place. Job 14:18*

These verses in Job are not prophetic as they do not discuss the time of the end. Rather, these verses may record Job's personal experiences and observations of actual earthquakes and collapsing mountains as he lived only a few centuries after the global flood. During this time, such occurrences may have been more frequent, as stresses within the earth's crust returned toward equilibrium after the upheaval caused by the breaking up the "*fountains of the great deep*" that had initiated the flood.

In the six hundredth year of Noah's life, in the second month, the seventeenth day of the month, on that day all the fountains of the great deep were broken up [baqa], and the windows of heaven were opened. Genesis 7:11

The use of the word [בָּקַע] *baqa*, meaning to rip, tear, break, divide, or split; all indicates that the earth experienced massive fracturing and earthquakes as mountains rose during the flood. The scriptures do not focus on describing this aspect of the flood as it would have occurred beneath the waves and was not observed from the safety of the ark.

It would have taken quite some time for the stresses causing such upheaval to gradually return to equilibrium. As previously discussed in chapter three, geologic data that I collected across western North America supports the concept that during the flood, mountains were pushed together and rose during widespread compressional stress. This would have allowed for the creation of ocean basins for the floodwaters to drain off the continents. Afterward, some mountains may have partially collapsed due to subsequent extensional stress, just like they did in central Wyoming. Both stress regimes would have caused *baqa*: extensive fracturing.

Stresses cause fractures to form and faults to slip, resulting in the rise and collapse of mountains. Earthquakes and volcanic activity result from these processes. Job lived in Arabia where the stress regime is still extensional to this day. And yet, the mountains collapsing, that Job seems so familiar with, do not happen frequently today. It is possible that the Creator, in His mercy, caused something to happen that then reduced the frequency of such occurrences and thus saved many lives throughout history. A possible way to provide this mercy would have been to move the orbit of the earth further from the sun.

In chapter nine, a change in the earth's orbit towards the sun was proposed so that prophecies of scorching heat might be fulfilled. In history however, I am hypothesizing just the opposite, that there was a change in orbit that was away from the sun.

Before discussing how such a change would be a mercy to life on earth, I want to discuss the possibility that clues may have been recorded that such an event did indeed happen. Such a change in the earth's orbit should result in sundials moving backwards. This is recorded in 2 Kings 20:10-11 as happening during the reign of King Hezekiah in approximately 700 BCE.

Following this, the next verse records a visit by ambassadors from Babylon. Babylonians were avid timekeepers, had probably heard of the abnormal movement observed on the sundial at Jerusalem, and wanted to further investigate even though the journey was far. It is well established that around that time, many cultures around the world began to develop calendars with 365 days in the year. Moving the earth backwards, away from the sun, would result in a longer orbit and thus a longer year. It is possible that before this, the calendar from creation had a much more simple 360 days in a year and 30 days in a month.

Scripture does not record the cause of the sundial moving backward, as it may not have been known. If the cause was a passing asteroid, then think of the fear of the heavens that humanity would have carried down through the intervening centuries. Not knowing or recording the cause may have been a mercy from the Creator.

There might be multiple beneficial effects of the earth being pulled into an orbit further away from the sun. The scriptures record that during the flood, the earth experienced unprecedented geologic upheaval which affected the biosphere and the atmosphere. When the "*windows of heaven*" were opened, the ideal configuration of the atmosphere, set up from creation, may have been changed. According to Genesis, human lifespans shortened significantly in the first few centuries after the flood. The reduced lifespans may have been associated with increasing harmful solar radiation due to the degradation of the atmosphere. Slowing this trend may have been a necessary intervention for the preservation of life.

After slipping further from the sun, the earth would have cooled. Cooling the earth would result in the crust contracting and increasing compressional stresses within it, creating more friction along faults. In order for blocks of land to slip along faults, even greater stresses would be required. This increased friction would result in fewer earthquakes. Volcanic activity would also diminish as the fractures through which molten rock flowed to the surface would be squeezed shut. An orbital adjustment would be a mercy from the Creator, saving many countless lives over the centuries.

If the earth were to experience the reversal of this mercy in the future, and instead have its orbit pulled closer to the sun, then global warming should significantly increase, just as prophesied. Because warming objects results in their expansion, the crust of the earth would expand allowing faults once again to slip easily and molten rock to flow upwards. The severity and frequency of earthquakes and volcanic eruptions would increase significantly.

By juxtaposing celestial and geologic events, Yeshua indicates that there is a relationship between the events in the heavens and those on earth just as proposed in this section. Especially noted is the odd placement of the mention of the sea and waves just after the sun, moon and stars, as recoded by Luke.

And there will be great earthquakes in various places… and there will be fearful sights and great signs from heaven…. And there will be signs in the sun, in the moon, and in the stars; and on the earth distress of nations, with perplexity, the seas and the waves roaring. Luke 21:11 & 25

Should the crust of the earth undergo future extension, many mountains still currently held up by dominant compressional stress regimes might very well collapse. This might be just what the prophets saw and recorded about time of the end. Not only might the mountains collapse and *mot*, or slip into the sea, but islands might also disappear since most of them are often just the tips of undersea mountain chains. Mountains, both on land and in the sea, are bounded by faults that may slip during extensional stress regimes. Collapsing mountains and islands are portrayed as the culmination of the seals and the bowls at the return of Yeshua.

...every mountain and island was moved out of its place. Revelation 6:14

Then every island fled away, and the mountains were not found. Revelation 16:20

The sixth seal also records that the wicked will prefer to die in this final great earthquake, running to hide in caves and even commanding the rocks and mountains to fall on them and hide them from the face of the coming rescuer.

For the righteous however, there is hope of protection from the Creator through these terrifying catastrophes. The righteous believe the prophecies and the promises that the Creator Himself will be our refuge during these catastrophic events.

God is our refuge and strength, a very present help in trouble. Therefore we will not fear, even though the earth be removed, and though the mountains be carried [mot] into the midst of the sea. Psalm 46:1-2.

As recorded by his follower Matthew, Yeshua also speaks of mountains moving, stating that those who have faith, even as little a mustard seed, may say to the mountains move and they will move. It does not require much faith to command mountains to move when it is a scientific possibility and already predicted! Yeshua reiterates this promise later where he is clearly referring to Psalm 46, and states that those who believe may cast mountains fully into the sea. At the time of the end, both the wicked and righteous command mountains to move—and the mountains actually respond—thus demonstrating the power of words for death or life.

So Yeshua said to them, "Because of your unbelief; for assuredly, I say to you, if you have faith as a mustard seed, you will say to this mountain, 'Move from here to there,' and it will move; and nothing will be impossible for you." Matthew 17:20

So Yeshua answered and said to them, "Assuredly, I say to you, if you have faith and do not doubt, … if you say to this mountain, 'Be removed and be cast into the sea,' it will be done." Matthew 21:21

The Messiah himself causes the collapse of the Mount of Olives. This prophecy of Zechariah and the last few chapters of Revelation are strikingly parallel. In Revelation 21:10, holy city that descends "*out of heaven*" is just so extensive that a great plain must be created for it to settle on. The measurements in Revelation are such that this city is large enough to be a refuge for countless righteous while stretching from the border of Turkey to the border of Yemen!

Noah's ark preserved eight righteous; riding the waves of the turbulent floodwaters that covered the earth. This city is sent by the Creator as a mercy to preserve the resurrected and rescued righteous from all of history. It settles on the surface of the earth which quakes like the waves of the sea. The wicked who assemble outside and seek to conquer the city, are instead destroyed in the hellish lake of fire that is spewed out by all of the volcanic eruptions engulfing the entire earth at that time.

And in that day His feet will stand on the Mount of Olives, which faces Jerusalem on the east. And the Mount of Olives shall be split in two, from east to west, making a very large valley; half of the mountain shall move toward the north and half of it toward the south. Zechariah 14:4

They went up on the breadth of the earth and surrounded the camp of the saints and the beloved city. And fire came down from God out of heaven and devoured them. Revelation 20:9

Aphelah & Araphel Darkness
Chapter 12

After the earthquakes split open the earth in great rifts, conduits are thus formed to bring magma from deep under the crust to the surface, exploding into the sky as fiery volcanic eruptions. The last two chapters have shown how warnings in the Hebrew scriptures may be linked back to the root cause of the earth's orbit slipping closer to the sun. There are still other, indirect geologic catastrophes that may have this same cause. This chapter will return to focus again on signs in Revelation while still placing the descriptions there in their context of the previous scriptures.

Darkness is described in both the fourth and fifth trumpets and it has already been mentioned that obscuring the celestial luminaries by "*smoke*" from the "*bottomless pit*" may be the result of increased volcanic activity. This darkness is even described as feeling painful in the fifth bowl. Comparing this to the story of the ten plagues in Egypt; the ninth plague was also of an unusual darkness that was felt.

Then the fifth angel poured out his bowl on the throne of the beast, and his kingdom became full of darkness; and they gnawed their tongues because of the pain. Revelation 16:10

Then YHWH said to Moses, "Stretch out your hand toward heaven, that there may be darkness

[choshek] over the land of Egypt, darkness which may even be felt [mashash]." So Moses stretched out his hand toward heaven, and there was thick darkness [choshek wa aphelah] in all the land of Egypt three days. They did not see one another; nor did anyone rise from his place for three days. But all the children of Israel had light in their dwellings.
Exodus 10:21-23

The word felt is translated from the word [משש] *mashash*, which means felt through, groped, or searched. How does one feel darkness? For the first time in scripture, the word [אפלה] *aphelah* is used to describe this darkness as thick and gloomy. What makes darkness thick? Also, why was this darkness limited geographically to the land of the Egyptians and not present where the Hebrews lived, and yet it lasted for three days? Answering these questions may help identify a potential cause of this plague of darkness. Understanding the cause of this past plague of darkness should help in knowing what to expect in the final plague of darkness.

An unusual darkness could be caused by the passage of a celestial object between the earth and the sun. During a solar eclipse, this is exactly what the moon does, but a solar eclipse lasts only a few minutes at most. In order to have darkness for three days, any other object passing between the earth and sun would have to be either far larger than the moon or traveling at a much slower speed. Even if such an object existed, because of how the earth's atmosphere refracts light, any objects passing would not result in total blackness. Instead, the darkness would be more like the twilight period just before sunrise, or just after sunset, where a few stars might still be visible. This is what happens with even total eclipses. More importantly, an astronomical event would not result in darkness that was limited to the Egyptians who had to feel, or *mashash* through it.

Heavy precipitation could be felt and a large storm could be limited geographically and yet last three days. The same could be the case for a severe dust storm. But these events are common enough that it raises the question of why Moses didn't just explicitly record the cause of the darkness as such. The vague description of unusual darkness indicates that he may have had difficulty finding words to properly describe this plague because it was not something commonly experienced. Moses is also believed to be the author of Job where numerous weather events are described. Job 37:11 even states that "*thick*" clouds are saturated with moisture. Yet here, the word for thick is not translated from the word *aphelah* as it is in the ninth plague. Using a different word in the book of Job may indicate that the thickness was not due to moisture.

In order to understand this darkness, uses of the word *aphelah* should be investigated elsewhere in the Hebrew scriptures in order to build a three-dimensional, full understanding. Joel and Zephaniah both describe the "*day of YHWH*" as a day of thick and gloomy, *aphelah* darkness.

A day of darkness and gloominess [choshek wa aphelah], a day of clouds and thick darkness [anan wa araphel]... Joel 2:2

...a day of darkness and gloominess [choshek wa aphelah], a day of clouds and thick darkness [anan wa araphel]. Zephaniah 1:15

These two prophecies and the account of the ninth plague in Exodus are the only places in the scriptures where the Hebrew phrase [חֹשֶׁךְ וַאֲפֵלָה] *choshek wa aphelah* is found. This is best translated as darkness, thick and gloomy. However, this is not the only phrase found in these two prophecies that connect back to Moses' records. There is also the phrase [עָנָן וַעֲרָפֶל] *anan wa araphel* which means clouds, heavy, thick and gloomy. In Deuteronomy this same phrase is found in the recounting of the making of the covenant at Mount Sinai. Here the phrase is expanded to [חֹשֶׁךְ עָנָן וַעֲרָפֶל] *choshek anan wa araphel* which adds the word for darkness, *choshek*, connecting back to the plague of darkness. In Exodus, the first account of the making of the covenant, the word *araphel* is also found alongside additional descriptions.

...the mountain burned with fire to the midst of heaven, with darkness, cloud, and thick darkness [choshek anan wa araphel]. Deuteronomy 4:11

...there were thunderings and lightnings, and a thick cloud [anan]... because YHWH descended upon it in fire. Its smoking ascended like the smoke of a furnace, and the whole mountain quaked greatly. Exodus 19:16 & 18

Now all the people witnessed the thundering, the lightning flashes... the mountain smoking... but Moses drew near the thick darkness [araphel] where God was. Exodus 20:18 & 21

With all these verses together, there may be enough pieces to assemble this puzzle and identify the cause of the plague of darkness. The events at Sinai describe a quaking mountain burning with fire and smoke to the midst of heaven; thus creating the same thick, gloomy clouds and darkness.

The ninth plague and the events at Mount Sinai are separated in time by about three months, so the event that caused the plague of darkness may not have been the same. However, what Moses may be trying to convey, is that there was a plague of an unusual darkness of a then-unknown cause; a cause which was later understood after witnessing similar thick and gloomy clouds at Sinai shortly thereafter.

Today, there are words to describe such events in geological terms. This would be described as a volcanic eruption and Mount Sinai identified as a volcano. The type of eruption likely being described is what geoscientists call a Plinian, or Vesuvian eruption, thus named because of the description provided by Pliny the Younger for the eruption of Mount Vesuvius in 79 CE that destroyed Pompeii. These violent eruptions are associated with thunder and lighting due to the rapid, upward movement of volcanic material which accumulates static electric charges. Strong earthquakes occur as molten rock moves toward the surface through fractures and violently erupts, sending immense volumes of thick, smoky ash into the atmosphere. This ash may take days to settle as a thick, gloomy darkness on the surrounding land. With the wind, it may travel far from where the volcano might been seen, heard, or felt. As the ninth plague describes, falling ash may also be limited in geographic extent and at the same time last for several days. It is understandable how the ancients might not have known the cause of the darkness without modern communication. These kinds of eruptions are rather common, an example being the 1980 eruption of Mount Saint Helens.

In the past and future plagues of darkness there must be something in the air that is causing a gloomy darkness that must be felt, painfully groped through, or *mashash*. Volcanic ash, hanging heavy, low, thick and gloomy might have been the cause of the ninth plague of the Exodus. As the fifth bowl describes, a thick cloud of volcanic ash might also be very painful. Depending on the proximity to the eruption, the ash might be hot enough to burn the skin and respiratory organs. Further away, the sharp particles of volcanic glass within the ash would still be a painful irritant to eyes and lungs. It should not be surprising that both past and future plagues of darkness may have similar causes because of their parallel descriptions.

Interestingly, others of the ten plagues might also be attributed to geologic activity associated with volcanos. The first plague where the water turned to "*blood*" might have been caused by a deadly, toxic chemical being released into the water through newly created fractures. Fish and other creatures would be killed by this toxic chemical, resulting in a bacterial bloom like a red tide, in which both the color and smell of the water would resemble blood. Amphibians, such as frogs, that are capable of living on land, would attempt to escape this polluted water. Not being able to return to the water, they would have eventually died, feeding a plague of flies which would lead to pestilences in livestock and humans.

Not all of the plagues may easily be explained as possibly beginning with volcanic activity and the power of the Creator in orchestrating these events should not be denied. The power of the Creator over creation is shown, even if a series of volcanic events was the cause of some of the plagues and the frightening occurrences at Mount Sinai. A balanced, careful approach is required to separate the natural phenomena from the supernatural. The account of Sinai also includes the sound of a trumpet and the voice of the Creator in addition to the natural noises. Natural noises associated with an eruption include: exploding, burning gases, rocks falling during earthquakes, and thunder; all of which would have been quite loud. Yet it is also recorded that the Creator spoke His covenant and was heard. To deny that there is a natural explanation for some of what happened at Sinai, or to deny the supernatural—to deny either—is to deny the power of the Creator over creation. The Creator alone has the power to speak and be heard over such displays of power.

Moses' record indicates that Sinai's possible volcanic eruption was not particularly extreme as he was able to ascend the mountain multiple times. It is not the purpose of this book to determine how explosive the eruption of Sinai may have been, nor even the mountain's location. A few scholars have attempted to identify the location of Mount Sinai based on its description as a volcano. However, these attempts have often tried to explain everything described in in a naturalistic way. No room is left for the miraculous and unexplainable. For example, the cloud that followed the Hebrews by day, and which became a pillar of fire by night, would not have been volcanic as it moved along with the Hebrews. At one point it even moved unnaturally between them and the Egyptians. Attempting to explain this cloud and everything else naturalistically just raises problems.

Understanding this should humble us and draw us to believe in the Creator. It should also give us great encouragement and peace during the future fifth plague of darkness when the Creator's power over creation is yet again to be demonstrated prior to the return of the Messiah. Just as the plagues of Exodus were a warning to Pharaoh to repent, so also will be the final warnings to the world at the time of the end. Pharaoh drowned after turning to his magicians instead of the Creator; we should not follow his example by turning to anyone else.

Because Revelation 13 describes the whole world as being a part of the beasts kingdom, then it may be concluded that this darkness is global. The number and size of volcanic eruptions required to plunge the world into a painful, gloomy darkness is astounding. And yet, just as the Hebrews were protected when the plagues afflicted the Egyptians, so the righteous will witness the final plagues and yet be delivered from them.

For the wicked, this soon-coming day will be terrifying. The Psalms speak of this day where, just as at Mount Sinai, "*clouds and darkness*" surround the Creator. For the righteous however, there are many promises of mercy from the Creator. The prophet Ezekiel admits the sheep will be scattered, but also promises that they will be delivered. When the entire earth trembles and mountains melt at His presence, there is still mercy and rescue for them.

While the prophets did not have the technical language of modern geoscience, they were certainly able to describe such mighty and awesome displays of the Creator's power over creation and link their descriptions, using parallel phrases, to wonderfully specific promises.

Clouds and darkness [anan wa araphel] surround Him… A fire goes before Him, and burns up His enemies round about. His lightnings light the world; the earth sees and trembles. The mountains melt like wax at the presence of YHWH, at the presence of YHWH of the whole earth. Psalm 97:1-5

As a shepherd seeks out his flock on the day he is among his scattered sheep, so will I seek out My sheep and deliver them from all the places where they were scattered on a cloudy and dark [anan wa araphel] day. Ezekiel 34:12

The Tohu wa Bohu Abyss
Chapter 13

I looked when He opened the sixth seal, and behold, there was a great earthquake; and the sun became black as sackcloth of hair, and the whole moon became like blood. And the stars [aster] of heaven fell to the earth, as a fig tree drops its late figs when it is shaken by a mighty wind. Then the sky receded as a scroll when it is rolled up, and every mountain and island was moved out of its place.
Revelation 6:12-14

The earth is quaking more strongly than ever experienced before. It is shaking so violently that its mountains and islands are collapsing. The ash from tremendous volcanic eruptions hangs heavy in the air, darkening the sun to appear as if seen through sackcloth, the particles in the air making the moon appear blood red. Both are apt descriptions for observing these luminaries through thick, gloomy clouds. Many remnants of celestial objects are still falling to the earth like dropping figs in an autumn wind. The seals, trumpets, and bowls describe a progression of events that culminate in this mighty crescendo on the soon-coming day of rescue.

And yet through all this, the Creator's voice is heard above the noise and chaos just as it was at Sinai. In parallel prophecies, the seventh trumpet and bowl both describe loud voices from heaven, heard from amidst the sounds of booming thunder.

These final prophecies are once again describing the Creator's ultimate power over creation.

Then the seventh angel sounded: and there were loud voices in heaven… and there were lightnings, noises, thundering, an earthquake, and great hail.
Revelation 11:15 & 19

Then the seventh angel poured out his bowl into the air, and a loud voice came out of the temple of heaven, from the throne, saying, 'It is done!' And there were noises and thunderings and lightnings; and there was a great earthquake, such a mighty and great earthquake as had not occurred since men were on the earth [ge]… Then every island fled away, and the mountains were not found. And great hail from heaven fell upon men, each hailstone about the weight of a talent…
Revelation 16:17-18, 20-21

While all this is happening on earth, heaven falls silent. The angels who never cease to sing the praises of the Creator have accompanied Yeshua to earth for the greatest rescue ever known. What a contrast between heaven and earth at that time!

When He opened the seventh seal, there was silence in heaven for about half an hour.
Revelation 8:1

John is not the only prophet who saw this day and records for us the appearance of the sun and moon, the shaking of the earth, and the fate of the wicked. Parallel phrases may also be found in many prophecies elsewhere in the scriptures. Jeremiah also describes darkness, earthquakes, and the fate of humanity. He is very clear that no man was to be found on earth at the end of this day. A phrase, [תֹהוּ וָבֹהוּ] *tohu wa bohu* is found here and only one other place: Genesis, where it describes the initial state of the earth prior to very first day of creation.

I beheld the earth, and indeed it was without form, and void [tohu wa bohu]; and the heavens, they had no light. I beheld the mountains, and indeed they trembled, and all the hills moved back and forth. I beheld, and indeed there was no man…
Jeremiah 4:23-25

The earth was without form, and void [tohu wa bohu]; and darkness was on the face of the deep…
Genesis 1:2

What Jeremiah might be telling us, is that the earthquakes and volcanic darkness will continue to the point that life for those not rescued will become unsustainable as the earth returns to the state it was in prior to the creation week. After giving the wicked as long as possible to turn away from death, the Creator sends the Messiah to return, at the last possible moment prior to certain death, to rescue his followers. At the end of this awesome day, no man is left: the wicked are dead under collapsed mountains by their own free choice. The righteous are caught up to heaven, along with the angels, to once again fill all paradise with the sounds of joyful praise to their Creator for His unfailing mercy. When the earth is left without humanity, the final creative act on the sixth day of creation is reversed. For the earth to return to its *tohu wa bohu*; pre-created, empty state however, each of the other days of creation must have also been reversed.

Recall that after the second bowl is poured out "*every living creature in the sea died*". The sea creatures along with the birds were created on the fifth day. The second bowl is thus a partial reversal of creation on the fifth day. However, the full reversal of the fifth day may not occur until later as "*all the birds were filled*" with the flesh of the wicked dead according to Revelation 19:21.

The sun, moon, and stars are "*struck*" when the fourth trumpet is blown, but they are not entirely destroyed. It is possible to interpret the Hebrew used in Genesis as describing the fourth day of creation to mean that these celestial luminaries already existed and were simply unveiled during the fourth day. The atmosphere may have been changed, allowing their light to reach the surface of the earth. This unveiling may be reversed as thick darkness once again veils them in prophecy.

After the first trumpet, "...*a third of the trees were burned up, and all green grass was burned up.*" Two thirds of the trees, created on the third day, survive this warning, but only for a time. Vegetation, just like the birds, are eventually destroyed when, as Peter states, the "*works*" on earth will be burned up, referring to "*all His work which God had created and made*" recorded in Genesis 2:3. Jeremiah confirms the impact of this day on the birds and fruitful land.

But the day of the Lord will come… in which the heavens will pass away with a great noise, and the elements will melt with fervent heat; both the earth [ge] and the works that are in it will be burned up. 2 Peter 3:10

…and all the birds of the heavens had fled. I beheld, and indeed the fruitful land was a wilderness, and all its cities were broken down at the presence of YHWH, by His fierce anger. Jeremiah 4:25-26

Peter also records that the heavens will pass away, the elements melting with fervent heat. This is not the first, nor is it the last prophecy of the ultimate destruction of the atmosphere. Parallels are found in the previous prophecies of Isaiah and also repeated in the sixth seal of Revelation and even the Quran.

All the host of heaven shall be dissolved, and the heavens shall be rolled up like a scroll… Isaiah 34:4

It is impossible to preserve any form of life without the atmosphere created on day two. It was created before any life as it is essential to all life. If the atmosphere were to vanish, even a few minutes before Yeshua returns, there would not be anyone left alive to rescue. What precise timing!

Returning to Jeremiah, he records that "*the heavens, they had no light*" indicating that even the light created on day one of creation may vanish. The picture thus presented of the events leading up to the return of the Messiah and its aftermath is stark indeed. The earth is once again shrouded in thick darkness with no light, no atmosphere, and no life. This final undoing of the days of creation, returning the earth to its *tohu wa bohu* state, is a dramatic consequence of the warnings sent at the end.

I highly encourage you now to take some time to read and meditate on Revelation 19:11-21:6. The passage opens with John seeing "*heaven opened*", a possible allusion to the receding of the sky at the return of the Messiah and the death of the wicked.

Then it is recorded that Satan will be chained for one thousand years in the "*bottomless pit*". These two words are translated from the single Greek word [ἀβύσσου] *abyssou* from which comes the English word abyss. This is the same word that was used to translate the *tohu wa bohu* of Genesis in the Greek translation of the Torah that was used during John's time. His context for this abyss would have been the *tohu wa bohu* of the earth prior to creation and to which Jeremiah states it will return with "*no man*".

...And they lived and reigned with Christ for a thousand years. But the rest of the dead did not live again until the thousand years were finished... Blessed and holy is he who has part in the first resurrection... Revelation 20:5-6

Those who live with the Messiah during the thousand years are those blessed to be part of the first resurrection and rescue of the righteous living at his return. The "*rest of the dead*" must be all those who preferred death and all other wicked who died throughout history. They will only be raised to face judgement when the thousand years are finished.

Without anyone left to deceive, Satan will be bound by chains of circumstance to the empty abyss that is earth in an uncreated, *tohu wa bohu* state. Satan will be given a thousand years to demonstrate his claim of equality with the Creator by creating from nothing something; anything. Satan will fail and thus be fully exposed as the ultimate deceiver and rebel that he is. The volcanic eruptions, unleashed in warning, culminate at the end of the thousand years with a molten lake of fire covering the earth. In this lake of fire, Satan, his angels, the wicked, and even death itself will be destroyed forever.

Then Death and Hades were cast into the lake of fire. This is the second death. And anyone not found written in the Book of Life was cast into the lack of fire. Revelation 20:14-15

Protection for the righteous is in the holy city that descends out of heaven, transporting them back to earth at the end of the thousand years. Only after the fire cleanses the entire earth of all traces of evil does the Creator re-create the earth to be an eternal paradise as only He creates such wonders.

Then, I, John, saw the holy city, New Jerusalem, coming down out of heaven from God… Then He who sat on the throne said, "Behold, I make all things new." And He said to me, "Write, for these words are true and faithful." Revelation 21:2 & 5

Shortening the Days
Chapter 14

Three of the trumpets and two of the bowls directly describe the consequences of impacts. The first is an impact in the sea, the second on land by an object named Wormwood, and a third unlocks the abyss. Diving deeply into Hebrew words and their meanings strongly supports the hypothesis that the earth's orbit will slip closer to the sun. The geologic consequences of such a drastic change may be the fulfilling of an additional three trumpets, four bowls, and the sixth seal. It is fitting that the majority of the signs in Revelation may thus be geologic since the book so often mentions the earth, or *ge*, in Greek.

The recording of so many Hebrew and Greek prophecies gives astonishing credibility to the main hypothesis of this book: a celestial event or object causes the earth's orbit to slip closer to the sun and results in catastrophic geologic warnings. One other consequence of the earth slipping closer to the sun would be a shortening the number of days in a year. The closer an object is to the object being orbited, the shorter the time required to make one full orbit. The length of the year is based on the time required for the earth to orbit the sun.

Do any of the prophecies of specific lengths of time also point to an orbital slip? In the scriptures, the most repeated time prophecy is recorded seven times, while all others are mentioned only once. In Daniel, this time prophecy is given twice as a *"time, times, and half a time"*. The parallel phrases about persecution of the saints during this time indicates that these verses are talking about the same period: a year, two years, and half a year; or 3.5 years.

He shall speak pompous words against the Most High, shall persecute the saints of the Most High, and shall intend to change times and law. Then the saints shall be given into his hand for a time, times, and half a time. Daniel 7:25

...it shall be for a time, times, and half a time; and when the power of the holy people has been completely shattered, all these things shall be finished. Daniel 12:7

Persecution of the saints is described again in Revelation 12 where the saints are symbolized by a pure, radiant woman who is provided a place in the wilderness where the Creator nourishes her.

Then the woman fled into the wilderness, where she has a place prepared by God, that they should feed her there one thousand two hundred and sixty day.... Now when the dragon saw that he had been cast to the earth [ge], he persecuted the woman who gave birth to the male child. But the woman was given two wings of a great eagle, that she might fly into the wilderness to her place, where she is nourished for a time and times and half a time, from the presence of the serpent.
Revelation 12:6 & 13-14

Once the time prophecy is given by quoting Daniel and once as 1260 days. These time periods should be equal, because they reference the same event, but they are not. The length of time it currently takes for the earth to make one complete orbit of the sun is 365.26 days. This is equal to 1278.41 days over the course of 3.5 years. The difference between the given times—that record the same event—is 18.41 days.

In order to account for this discrepancy, many make the assumption that the prophecies must be using a Jewish calendar and then make the false claim that the Jewish calendar has 360 days in a year. The Jewish calendar used today, the Hillel II calendar, does not have 360 days, only 354. As needed, an entire leap month is sometimes added. This calendar is based on an older calendar, but uses calculations rather than observations.

The calendar used by the prophets, including Daniel and John, also did not have 360 days in it. Their calendar was a true, luni-solar calendar based on observation. While the spring equinox fixed the beginning of the year, each of twelve months began with the sighting of the new, crescent moon just after sunset and lasted either 29 or 30 days until the next sighting. To keep the months in their proper season, every few years, a thirteenth month would need to be added before the year began again at the spring equinox.

A few are aware that these calendars are not 360 days in length and so have come up with an imaginary "prophetic" calendar with 360 days and 30 days in a month. This "prophetic" calendar relies on circular reasoning to explain the discrepancy in the length of times given. One first assumes that the length of years used in prophecy is 360 days and months are 30 days, even though there is nothing scriptural to support this idea other than the need to make these time prophecies equal.

Instead, of making such an assumption, this book hypothesizes that a change in the orbit of the earth closer to the sun must happen in order to bring these time prophecies into alignment. A "prophetic" calendar is an assumption that can never be tested while this hypothesis is testable, even if only testable in the future. Proposing a hypothesis that resolves the discrepancy in the length of time is the rigorous scientific approach. If a strictly literal interpretation is used, then a logical conclusion would be that at no point in history have these time prophecies been literally fulfilled because the year has been 365.26 days since long before they were given.

Three mentions of this time prophecy remain and are found surrounding Revelation 12 as part of the same passage. Revelation 11 and 13 provide a description of what the wicked are doing during the time the saints are in the wilderness. In Revelation 11 the time is mentioned twice, once describing what the wicked are doing, and another describing how two witnesses are endeavoring to reason with them during this time.

...And they will tread the holy city underfoot for forty-two months. And I will give power to my two witnesses, and they will prophesy one thousand two

hundred and sixty days, clothed in sackcloth.
Revelation 11:2-3

And he was given a mouth speaking great things
and blasphemies, and he was given authority to
continue for forty-two months. Revelation 13:5

Once again the time is given as 1260 days, showing that these three mentions are also parallel to the previous four. Twice the time period is given as 42 months, introducing yet another inequality as 42 months is not equal to 1260 days. A month is currently 29.53 days and since the time that these prophecies were given, 42 months has been equal to 1240.26 days over the course of 3.5 years. This is 19.74 days short of 1260: the discrepancy between months and days is not even the same as between days and years!

Because these time prophecies are parallel, they are predicting that at some point, 3.5 years will equal 42 months and also 1260 days, not just one or the other. There may be ways in which to resolve these two discrepancies that do not require making circular assumptions. Certain events must happen in the physical realm, either the rotation of the earth will need to slow so that the days lengthen, its orbit will need to move closer to the sun to shorten the number of days in a year, or some combination of these two. Also, the orbit of the moon must change to alter the length of the month accordingly. These might be theoretically possible and would be observable natural events.

The earth currently spins at 1040.42 miles per hour at the equator. This rate would need to slow to 1025.44 miles per hour for there to be 360 days in a year. The lunar year is currently 354.36 days, about six days shorter than a 360 day year while the solar year is about five days longer. In order for the month to have exactly 30 days, the rotational speed of the earth would actually have to speed up to 1056.98 miles per hour. The earth cannot achieve 360 days in a year and 30 days in a month simply by changing its rotational speed. For one it would have to slow down and for the other speed up!

The calculated changes in these rotational speeds for the earth are quite large differences and would be equivalent to adjusting the length of the day by over 20 minutes either way. Theoretically, it might be possible for an impact, or series of impacts, to change the rotational speed of the earth to this degree. A good question for an astrophysicist would be if the earth could withstand large enough impacts to change its rotational speed by this much and still exist to sustain life. Regardless, there is still the issue of simultaneously adjusting the length of the year and of the month. This cannot be done by only changing the rotational speed of the earth. While an impact, or even a series of them, could make minor adjustments to the rotational speed of the earth, it is quite clear that something more is also required to obtain equality among the three measurements of the same time in these prophecies.

Therefore, this book proposes that these time prophecies cannot be fulfilled without some kind of celestial event or a large and heavy celestial object, passing near enough to earth to adjust its orbit by gravitationally pulling it closer to the sun. A rogue planet may be to massive. Since comets are composed of ice, their density might be insufficient to have enough gravitational pull. The hypothesis of a large, heavy asteroid seems most reasonable, especially since it fits with other impacts mentioned in Revelation as well as the Greek word *aster*.

This asteroid would have to adjust the orbits of both the earth and the moon simultaneously in order to obtain equality in the time prophecies. The earth would have to be pulled closer to the sun at the same time that the earth is also pulled further from the moon. It makes sense that a massive enough asteroid, gravitationally pulling the earth, would also pull on the moon and so it would have to be further away from the asteroid in order to not be pulled as much as the earth.

An objects gravitational pull is determined by both its mass and distance from the object its gravity is acting on. In order to achieve 360 days in a year, and also 30 days in a month, the position of the objects relative to each other is also critical. There may not be a unique solution to this problem as a whole range of masses, distances, and positions might result in the needed changes to both the earth and the moon's orbits. Models of various scenarios like these could be made and run by astrophysicists to determine possibility. My expertise however, is the effects on the earth's crust as it expands from the heat of it being closer to the sun. These geologic consequences being the main focus of this book: the increasing severity and frequency of earthquakes associated with tremendous volcanic eruptions and the collapse of mountains.

Another complicating factor is the potential for the adjustment to the orbit to occur in stages if the asteroid is actually composed of a series of smaller asteroids like the comet Shoemaker-Levy 9. There is already the potential for multiple asteroids present in prophecy with the three direct impacts described in the trumpet warnings. A single larger asteroid would certainly gain attention as a warning, however, a series of several slightly smaller asteroids, would be ominous as well, and might prove a mercy should a single adjustment to earth's orbit be too catastrophic.

These successive gravitational pulls from a series of passing asteroids, or even the single pull hypothesized, might result in orbits of 360 days for the earth and 30 days for the moon. Also helping to accomplish this might be slight adjustments to the earth's rotational speed caused by the impacts. This may return the length of the calendar back to what it was originally created to be and which may have continued until the sundial moved backwards during the reign of King Hezekiah.

In summary, there is a natural explanation for most of the trumpet warnings and bowl plagues of Revelation that pieces together the most referenced time prophecy in all of scripture: the final 3.5 years with a major celestial event like a massive asteroid, passing near to the earth. As it speeds by, it pulls the earth and moon into new orbits. This would have to occur at least 3.5 years before the return of Yeshua in order for the time prophecies to be fulfilled. This means that this asteroid may be passing earth about the same time as the trumpet warnings are given; so possibly with a relative timing just before, during, or after the direct impacts.

The Creator of the universe, in His mercy, may have sent these multiple celestial warnings speeding across the universe at just the right spacing between them to fulfill His prophetic warnings at just the right time. He alone is all-knowing to predict these events thousands of years in advance and all-powerful to bring these events to completion. In His mercy He warns us in advance so that when we see these fearful sights in the heavens, we will not need to be afraid, but instead look forward to the soon return of Yeshua with great anticipation.

Remember the former things of old, for I am God, and there is no other; I am God, and there is none like Me, declaring the end from the beginning, and from ancient times things that are not yet done, saying, "My counsel shall stand, and I will do all My pleasure." Isaiah 46:9-10

Finally realizing the possibility that so many prophecies may be fulfilled due to the earth's orbit being adjusted answered a burning question I had since a teenager; the question of how the Creator might shorten the days. Mark records what Yeshua had to say about this for our benefit.

And unless the Lord had shortened those days, no flesh would be saved; but for the elect's sake, whom He chose, He shortened the days. Mark 13:20

The shortening of the final 3.5 years from 1278 days to 1260 days by an orbital adjustment now provides my curiosity a reasonable explanation for what Yeshua was talking about. It also tells me how much the days are shortened by during the time of the end. Eighteen days is not a very long time. However, when the whole world is rising up to wipe out the saints, the remnant of the righteous elect, then eighteen days may be the difference between life and death. Yeshua seems to be telling us that if the world lasted a mere eighteen days longer, there would be no one left alive on earth to rescue.

In the Creator's wonderful mercy, He has given as much time as possible for the wicked to repent. And then, at the very last moment possible in earth's history, He sends Yeshua the Messiah to finally return and rescue His faithful sheep. HalleluYah!

GEOLOGY OF THE MIDDLE EAST
Section IV

"If it had not been YHWH who was on our side,
When men rose up against us,
Then they would have swallowed us alive,
When their wrath was kindled against us;
Then the waters would have overwhelmed us,
The stream would have gone over our soul;
Then the swollen waters would have gone over our
soul." Blessed be YHWH,
Who has not given us as prey to their teeth.
Our soul has escaped
as a bird from the snare of the fowlers;
The snare is broken, and we have escaped.
Our help is in the name of YHWH,
Who made heaven and earth.

Psalm 124:2-8

Foreshadows of Prophecy
Chapter 15

The Creator designed the laws which govern the universe, both the physical and spiritual realms. When an event occurs that surpasses our ability to explain it, we are right to marvel at His power over creation. Miracles are not what happens when the Creator breaks the laws He designed, rather, they are simply the term we give to supernatural events beyond our current understanding of His laws. As our understanding deepens, some events that were formerly considered supernatural may be found to have natural explanations. Being able to understand how He accomplishes His purposes in the physical creation does not diminish the glory He is due as the Creator.

In the previous section, global geologic signs were investigated while this section will focus on the Middle East: Levant and Arabia. Previously, the final cleansing of the world with fire was compared to the global flood of Noah. This cleansing is one of many events in prophecy that have parallels in the stories recorded by the scriptures. The geologic study of this flood is not the study of a miracle, but of the evidence that it left in the earth's broken surface. In the same way, some stories that will be discussed in this section may be considered miraculous and yet they have elements that have geologic explanations. A supernatural cause for these events: the power of the Creator, does not preclude a natural explanation for how they happened in the physical creation. This section will investigate some stories that happened in the land of the prophets and how they might also parallel prophecies to be fulfilled in the near future.

What is wondrously fascinating to me as a geoscientist are that the subtle clues hinting at past geologic events are all consistent with the historical and current geologic setting of the land wherein they occurred. Scripture records earthquakes, collapsing mountains, and rifting, which all indicate a regime of extensional stress.

The Levant and Arabia are situated along a rift valley that extends from north of Galilee, south along the Jordan River and the Dead Sea, and also forms the narrow trend of the Red Sea. This large rift system is the result of the extensional stress that is caused by the African and Arabian tectonic plates; large portions of earth's crust that are moving away from each other ever since the crust was broken up during the global flood. This divergent movement causes earthquakes as the land splits apart. Faults are found on either side of this rift valley along with evidence for the collapse of mountains and volcanic eruptions. The stories in scripture are consistent with the geologic record!

If deep enough, the fractures split open along the margins of this rift valley may become conduits for volcanic material to violently erupt out of them and destroy whatever it rains down on. Today, it is still possible to find ash and human bones at the sites of the fiery overthrow of Sodom and Gomorrah. These wicked cities are situated near the major fault trends on the eastern shores of the Dead Sea where volcanic material may also be found nearby.

Then YHWH rained brimstone and fire on Sodom and Gomorrah, from YHWH out of the heavens.
Genesis 19:24

Even when not erupting molten rock, rifts may also be very destructive. A spectacularly example of this was observed when a wide rift cut through an olive orchard during the February 2023 earthquake near Antakya, Turkey. A lengthy rift also formed in the wilderness near Al Majma'ah, Saudi Arabia in February 2018. Similar rifting may have been what killed Korah, Dathan, and Abiram in their wilderness rebellion which was also in Arabia.

"...the ground split apart under them, and the earth opened its mouth and swallowed them up..."
Numbers 16:31-32

The story does not describe the earthquake necessary to cause the rifting as often scripture is more concerned with the consequences of events rather than their initial cause. In the story of Sodom and Gomorrah, the "*brimstone and fire*" is described as coming from "*the heavens*" even though the initial source was probably from the earth and the eruption itself was probably not observed.

The Hebrew crossings of the Red Sea and the Jordan River were probably also associated with major earthquakes. I personally believe that it took more than just the strong east wind mentioned in

Exodus 14:21-22 to make the Red Sea crossing possible on "*dry ground*". While the wind held back the sea, dry rock from below the thick muds forming the seafloor may have become exposed due to fault movement. Joshua 3:16 records that the flow of the Jordan River was stopped from the village of Adam all the way to the Dead Sea south of Jericho. An aftershock may have been responsible for toppling the walls of Jericho a week later. Collapsed debris has blocked the flow of the Jordan River many times in recorded history, most recently in July 1927, and many nearby cities have been destroyed at various times.

In 2 Kings 2, two additional crossings of the Jordan River are recorded. First by Elijah and Elisha and then again when only Elisha's returned. After a possible aftershock allowed for Elisha to return, a third aftershock may have occurred at the same time he threw salt into Jericho's spring of bitter water. This aftershock may have created new fractures in the rock which allowed the water to originate from a new layer of rock containing sweet water. This spring still flows sweet today.

These stories may foreshadow what is yet to happen in that land. The prophet Habakkuk speaks accurately of the geology of this area in predicting a future earthquake that will cause extensive damage. The countries he mentions are on either side of the Red Sea, the epicenter of many small earthquakes. Cushan is modern Sudan in Africa and on the other side is Midian, the parallel region of Saudi Arabia.

Yes, the everlasting mountains were shattered, the ancient hills collapsed.... I saw the tents of Cushan under distress, the tent curtains of the land of Midian were trembling.... The mountains saw You and quaked... Habakkuk 3:6,7, & 10 (NASB®)

Another place where prophesied earthquakes will occur is Jerusalem. As previously mentioned, in chapter eleven, Zechariah predicts that the Mount of Olives will finally collapse into a broad plain. From this single verse it is possible to determine that the extensional stress that has been present in this land since at least the time of Job, will continue until all things are re-created in the earth made new.

An earthquake large enough to result in the collapse of a mountain is also certainly large enough to throw down the massive stones from the time of Yeshua that still make up the Western Wall less than a kilometer away. These large stones still stand one atop each other and include the "Western Stone". At over 250 tonnes it is one of the heaviest stones ever moved without modern machinery.

These things which you see—the days will come in which not one stone shall be left upon another that shall not be thrown down. Luke 21:6

...all men who are on the face of the earth shall shake at My presence. The mountains shall be thrown down, the steep places shall fall, and every wall shall fall to the ground. Ezekiel 38:20

This prophecy of Yeshua was partially fulfilled when Roman conquerors threw down the stones of the temple building onto the street below where they may still be seen in heaps today. These prophecies however, are still awaiting their ultimate fulfillment as Ezekiel further predicts that "*every wall shall fall*". Throwing down this wall along with the surrounding mountains will require an earthquake the scale of which has not yet been felt.

It is interesting to discover that there was a 3.5 year period from the time when Roman soldiers first surrounded Jerusalem in the fall of 66 CE until Titus returned and finally conquered the city in the spring of 70 when some stones were thrown down. In this same prophecy, Yeshua also warned his followers to "*flee to the mountains*" when they saw the city surrounded by armies. This initial retreat of the Roman army was a mercy that allowed the followers of Yeshua the opportunity to escape.

But when you see Jerusalem surrounded by armies, then know that its desolation is near. Then let those who are in Judea flee to the mountains…. and Jerusalem will be trampled by gentiles until the times of the gentiles are fulfilled. Luke 21:20-21 & 24

Fleeing, without hesitation, was the correct response to seeing this warning sign as there was no way for them to know, at the time, that the final fulfillment of this prophecy is still to happen. When Roman soldiers first appeared, the followers of Yeshua immediately left Jerusalem. They fled north-east, to the city of Pella in the mountainous region of the Decapolis, just outside the area under control of Jewish rebels and across the Jordan River.

The massive stones of the Western Wall still stand however, indicating that Jerusalem is still to be surrounded by armies again. This future conquest of Jerusalem was later predicted again in the book of Revelation, associated with the final 3.5 year period. There, John used parallel wording to Yeshua before: the holy city being trampled underfoot by "*gentiles*".

But leave out the court which is outside the temple, and do not measure it, for it has been given to the gentiles. And they will tread the holy city underfoot for forty-two months. Revelation 11:2

Matthew records additional words of Yeshua to link this warning to "*flee to the mountains*" with the prophecies of Daniel where this trampling imagery is first used along with describing the "*desolation*" that is the absence of the *tamiyd*.

"Therefore when you see the 'abomination of desolation,' spoken of by Daniel the prophet, standing in the holy place" (whoever reads, let him understand), "then let those who are in Judea flee to the mountains. Matthew 24:15-16

…"How long will the vision be, concerning the daily [tamiyd] ~~sacrifices~~ *and the transgression of desolation, the giving of both the sanctuary and the host to be trampled underfoot?" Daniel 8:13*

Tamiyd, as discussed in the second chapter, is all about taking time to maintain a relationship with the Creator through praise, prayer, and study of the scriptures. This relationship is the focus of constant attack and it is not unreasonable to believe that it may become outlawed once again, just as it was for Daniel in the story of the lion's den. At the time of the end, those righteous who desire to maintain this relationship may be forced to flee from an army set on trampling this *tamiyd* and causing desolation.

Hopefully, by using the methods for three-dimensional thinking, you may once again see how multiple verses may be connected together using parallel phrases. The surrounding of Jerusalem by armies, the trampling of the city by "*gentiles*", the taking away of the *tamiyd* and the "*abomination of desolation*", and the flight to the mountains; all are adjacent puzzle pieces giving a prophetic picture.

When it comes to the final 3.5 years, there is Jerusalem, the stated starting point, the path of the flight to the wilderness, and the place of refuge. All places have geologic settings and these will be fully investigated in the next chapter. As the followers of Yeshua were not in Jerusalem when the Romans conquered it, so the righteous at the time of the end will not be in in the city, but elsewhere. In His mercy, the Creator has provided clues to where refuge may be found until Yeshua the Messiah returns to rescue his followers.

Swallowing Rising Floods
Chapter 16

After Revelation 11 records that the holy city is yet to be trampled by "*gentiles*" for 3.5 years, the following chapter records that the righteous will flee to a place of refuge during this time. These righteous are described by using the symbol of a pure woman who flees "*into the wilderness*". It may be possible to identify this wilderness' location by finding adjacent puzzle pieces with parallel verses from scripture as well as subtle clues from geology.

But the earth [ge] helped the woman, and the earth [ge] opened its mouth and swallowed up the flood which the dragon had spewed out of his mouth.
Revelation 12:16

If you are beginning to practice the art of three-dimensional thinking, then something in this verse should sound familiar. Hopefully your brain is already reaching for the puzzle piece containing the story of Korah's wilderness rebellion where also "*the earth opened its mouth and swallowed them up*". The only difference is that in the phrase in Numbers the earth opens its mouth to swallow up Korah and his rebel companions while in the future it opens to swallow "*the flood*". By its parallel choice of phrase, Revelation is showing the context of this prophecy is this story. Certainly both story and prophecy occur in the same extensional stress regime. This may be a major clue that the place where this future rifting will happen is the same wilderness as before.

Often, when the scriptures speak of just "*the wilderness*" and provide no other identifying names, the writers are referring to the wilderness where the Hebrews were nourished by manna from heaven and given water from the rock as found in Exodus 16-17. The Creator also feeds and nourishes in the future wilderness described in Revelation.

Further references to the story in Exodus are given when Revelation uses the same imagery of the "*eagle's wings*" to metaphorically transport the righteous quickly and safely, just like the Hebrews were when they escaped Egypt.

But the woman was given two wings of a great eagle, that she might fly into the wilderness to her place, where she is nourished... Revelation 12:14

You have seen what I did to the Egyptians, and how I bore you on eagles' wings and brought you to Myself. Exodus 19:4

As discussed in the previous chapter, the starting place for the future flight of the righteous is directly stated as Jerusalem. It is possible that the ending point of their flight, the place of refuge, is the same Exodus wilderness. However, by not directly giving the ending place for this flight, its location is subtly veiled. This is a mercy to protect those who find their way to this hidden place of refuge.

This wilderness is across the Jordan River from Jerusalem and so anyone fleeing there must cross the river north-east of the city. The story of the followers of Yeshua crossing this river to flee to the mountains appears to also foreshadow the righteous crossing this river once again in their future flight.

The time prophecies of the final 3.5 years, as discussed in chapter fourteen, connects Daniel 7-12 with Revelation 11-13 just like the locks and keys of puzzle pieces. These passages are primarily dealing with the great controversy between the wicked army of those who choose to accept the lies of Satan, and the righteous who choose to follow Yeshua and trust in the mercy of the Creator.

Both passages speak of persecution of the saints. In both, the symbol of a terrible beast is used to describe the character of the kingdom marshaling this army. Ultimately, this kingdom will be destroyed: "*given to the burning flame*" (Daniel 7:11) and "*cast alive into the lake of fire burning with brimstone*" (Revelation 19:20); but not before devouring "*the whole earth*" (Daniel 7:23) and being given authority over "*every tribe, tongue, and nation*" (Revelation 13:7) for 3.5 years.

The identity of this kingdom is not nearly as important however, as knowing where its army will be so that it may be avoided. In Daniel 11 the title "*King of the North*" is used to describe the leader of this kingdom. The final verses of this chapter predict a great, final conflict and a list of countries is given. All of the countries listed as following this king, being conquered, or escaping, are in the Middle East.

He shall also enter the Glorious Land, and many countries shall be overthrown; but these shall

escape from his hand: Edom, Moab, and the
prominent people of Ammon. He shall stretch out his
hand against the countries, and the land of Egypt
shall not escape. He shall have power over the
treasures of gold and silver, and over all the
precious things of Egypt; also the Libyans and
Ethiopians shall follow at his heels. Daniel 11:41-43

Interestingly, Edom, Moab and Ammon, which all compose the modern country of Jordan, are the ones that "*escape from his hand*". These are all on the east side of the Jordan River, the same side that the early followers of Yeshua found refuge on after fleeing Jerusalem. Egypt, which does not escape, is listed twice giving it special focus. Egypt is not the ultimate conquest however, the "*Glorious Land*" is.

And he will pitch the tents of his royal pavilion
between the seas and the beautiful Holy Mountain;
yet he will come to his end, and no one will help him.
Daniel 11:45 (NASB®)

The "*Glorious Land*" is where the "*beautiful holy mountain*" rises between the Dead Sea and the Mediterranean Sea. These are fitting adjectives for the land of Daniel's homeland and for the mountain on which the temple Solomon built had stood. Daniel is predicting here the future conquest of Jerusalem just as Yeshua and John would also.

But news from the east and the north shall trouble
him; therefore he shall go out with great fury to
destroy and annihilate many. Daniel 11:44

In this verse, that was previously skipped over, this king is predicted to *"go out"*, to the north-east. This is the same direction that the righteous would need to flee to get across the Jordan River and thus reach the safety of the *"mountains"* mentioned by Yeshua and then the refuge in *"the wilderness"* of the Exodus alluded to by John. This king does not succeed in conquering the righteous however.

So the serpent spewed water out of his mouth like a flood after the woman, that he might cause her to be carried away by the flood. Revelation 12:15

Then he said to me, "The waters which you saw, where the harlot sits, are peoples, multitudes, nations, and tongues. Revelation 17:15

Revelation states that the waters symbolize a multitude of people from many nations. Joel predicts that a *"northern army"* will be destroyed between the seas and facing east, just as the *"King of the North"* in Daniel would be if he was pursuing the righteous with his army as they flee Jerusalem.

I will remove far from you the northern army, and will drive him away into a barren and desolate land, with his face toward the eastern sea and his back toward the western sea... Joel 2:20

However, here is an example of the potential to interpret prophecy literally as well. Rifts that open to swallow an army are also capable of swallowing literal floods of water. Since the purpose of this book is to investigate geologic fulfillments, this possibility needs to be investigated. Just as Pharaoh and his army drowned in the Red Sea, this future king and his army may also be destroyed attempting to cross the Jordan River which trickles at the bottom of the same rift valley that forms that sea. As discussed, the extensional stress regime of this rift valley and the entire region does allow the earth's crust to rift and split open.

So are the flood waters in Revelation from the Jordan River, or are they greater? If the earth's orbit did slip closer to the sun just before this time, the result would be extreme global warming that would likely melt the polar ice sheets and glaciers. If all of the ice around the world were to melt, it is estimated that sea level would rise by at least 65 meters. Many low-lying coastal cities and entire places like Florida, Bangladesh, the Netherlands, and other vast areas would become completely submerged.

Just across the Jordan River from the ancient city of Pella, the Jezreel Valley trends north-west all the way to the Mediterranean. Roughly in the middle of this valley is its highest point at only about 60 meters above sea level. Should sea level rise above this, then the entire Jordan River valley would flood from the Sea of Galilee to the Dead Sea. Ezekiel even predicts that the Dead Sea will be healed and contain the same fish found in the Mediterranean, thus implying a connection between them.

…Their fish will be of the same kinds as the fish of the Great Sea, exceedingly many. Ezekiel 47:10

At its deepest, where the Jordan River meets the Dead Sea, this valley is 470 meters below sea level. The additional weight of 535 meters of sea water would certainly cause slip on the normal faults bounding this valley. In extensional stress regimes, the maximum compressive stress is vertical. Adding the pressure of such deep water, while at the same time expanding the crust of the earth as discussed in chapter eleven, would cause massive earthquakes of unprecedented scale.

The entire filling of this valley might occur in stages where it partially floods and then earthquakes expose dry land again just as what might have taken place when the Hebrews crossed the Red Sea. Rifts may form along the margins of the valley, opening to swallow both literal floods and the army these floods symbolized in prophecy.

Think of the joy the righteous experience to be so awesomely delivered from their persecutors! If in His mercy, the Creator of the universe may cause the earth to slip toward the sun, melt enough ice to flood a particular valley, and thus deliver His people, then all praise is rightfully His. After witnessing this miraculous way the Creator uses the geologic forces of His creation to deliver them, then their belief in the soon return of Yeshua the Messiah will be greatly strengthened. Despite even greater geologic signs still to come, hope will replace fear as they await their final rescue.

The Time of the End
Chapter 17

Most geologic investigations are incomplete without discussing at least relative time. There are two ways of conceptualizing time. Relative time is the time relationship between events while absolute time is just the date associated with an event. An example of relative time from geology would be to compare a fault to the layers of rock containing the fault. To determine relative time, a geologist would first determine the order of the layers within the rock. The oldest always begins at the bottom because new sediment may only be deposited on top of an existing layer, never below. A fault would have to be younger than the layers that it breaks and older than the layers that it does not break. Relative time is always based on a relationship between two events, in this case, the deposition of the layers followed by the faulting.

The assigning to layers of rock absolute time: dates of millions upon millions of years, is based on three faulty assumptions. Radiometric dating only works if 1) the rate of radiometric decay of isotopes is constant, but it is known now that it may change slightly; 2) there has been no isotopes gained or lost over time, a doubtful proposition if the rock is truly as old as it is claimed; and 3) that the original ratio of isotopes is known, which is a near impossibility that requires additional assumptions in order to be made. Radiometric dating methods have been shown to be unreliable as newly formed deposits created during the Mount Saint Helens volcanic eruption in May of 1980 were dated at hundreds of thousands of years old.

Assigning absolute dates to prophetic time is just as faulty. Over and over again, dates have been set for the return of Yeshua that have been based on faulty interpretations of prophecy; proven faulty as Yeshua has still not returned. His return is eminent, but no absolute dates may be determined for either the beginning of the final 3.5 years or their ending.

The chronology of years recorded first in the scriptures, and then later in history, indicates that there has been just under six thousand years from the creation of life till today. The final thousand years before eternity begins should begin with the return of Yeshua to rescue his followers in the next few years. It is not the purpose of this book however, to discuss this chronology, nor when these geologic events discussed in this book will occur, nor when Yeshua will return, even though it must be soon.

It is possible however, to discuss the relative timing; the relationship between events described in prophecy. The relative time relationship between the second trumpet and bowl is discussed in chapter eight. A third of sea creatures die after the trumpet is blown which can only happen before they all die when the bowl is poured out. A similar relationship between exists between the third trumpet and the third bowl as already discussed. By the time the seventh trumpet is blown and the seventh bowl is poured out, the relative timing is virtually the same as the both the trumpets and bowls conclude with the same event, the return of Yeshua. Likewise, the seals also conclude with the return of Yeshua. Thus, the seals, trumpets, and bowls all occur in a short amount of overlapping time relative to each other.

The relative timing of the final 3.5 years with these warning signs may also be determined even if their absolute timing cannot be. Since this time also concludes just before Yeshua returns, then these years should overlap with these signs. However, if the majority of the warning signs in Revelation have a single root cause as hypothesized, then that cause must happen before these years begin. The earth's orbit must slip closer to the sun in order to shorten the days before the 3.5 years begin as discussed in chapter fourteen. Since the majority of the warning signs are the geologic consequences of the earth slipping, then it is probable that these signs begin just before the 3.5 years and continue building in intensity throughout them.

Many times I have used the phrase "*the time of the end*" in order to indicate that the event being discussed occurs relatively close to the end. This phrase comes from Daniel, where it introduces the verses describing the final conquest of the "*King of the North*" as discussed in the previous chapter.

At the time of the end the King of the South shall attack [nagach] him; and the King of the North shall come against him like a whirlwind, with chariots, horsemen, and with many ships; and he shall enter the countries, overwhelm them, and pass through.
Daniel 11:40

153

Is the final war described in this passage the same as the one described when the second seal is opened and the red horse is rode forth? Relative timing suggests that it may be. Daniel predicts that this war begins with an "*attack*", translated from the word [נגח] *nagach*. In all thirteen instances this word appears in the scriptures, it is used in the context of horned animals and the better translation is to gore. Gores are deep, penetrating wounds that often end in death due to the severity of the trauma inflicted. In Revelation, the parallel for this goring is likely the "*deadly wound*".

And I saw one of his heads as if it had been mortally wounded, and his deadly wound was healed. And all the world marveled and followed the beast…. and he was given authority to continue for forty-two months.
Revelation 13:3 & 5

After this deadly goring is healed, there is a deadly response. Many nations follow this beast into the final world war. Those who take up the sword will die, not just by the sword, but also by famine and pestilence. The war is not only a political conflict, but is also religious as the beast will attempt to change the Creator's "*times and law*". The word "*times*" in Daniel 7:25 is translated from the Aramaic word [זמן] *zeman* which is the word still used to describe the times for the *tamiyd* prayers that Jews offer today.

The relative timing of the fifth seal and the persecution of the righteous may then coincide with the trampling underfoot of Jerusalem by "*gentiles*" who are led by the "*King of the North*". For a limited time the wicked will persecute and kill some of those who follow Yeshua's example of love, peace, and submission to the Creator's laws. Many make their escape to "*the wilderness*". The war begins the "*time of the end*", proceeds rapidly like a "*whirlwind*", and culminates in the conquest of Jerusalem. The result is "*desolation*" and the beginning of the 3.5 years. The way John inserted the passages dealing with this time span in between the trumpets and bowls is yet another way of subtly indicating that their relative timing overlaps.

By looking at relative timing, a clearer picture of the mercy of the Creator may be seen. The war that humanity begins because of greed and hatred might be the reason why the Creator then begins to send warning after warning in the form of celestial objects and their following geologic consequences. Great signs in the heavens will be sent speeding across the universe, impacting or possibly passing near earth, warning humanity to look up for their rescue instead of at each other with murderous hate.

Regardless of exact timing, we know that these geologic events are coming soon and will culminate in the earth returning to the abyss of its uncreated state, the *tohu wa bohu*, devoid of all life as the wicked destroy themselves and the righteous are rescued.

The "*time of the end*" may be beginning very soon. Even now, turmoil is increasing rapidly as available resources decrease. Financial and political instability within nations is likewise being directed outwards and new wars are beginning. Although it is not known just how long it might be before the stage is fully set for the final war described in prophecy to begin, it must be very soon.

The most important question to ask is if we will choose to attempt to save ourselves and join with either army, taking resources from others, or if we will join with the righteous in keeping the Creator's laws of love and peace. The righteous believe in the protection and mercy of the Creator. They do not have to fight, steal resources, and kill others to preserve themselves. Instead, they choose to flee to the wilderness for the final 3.5 years where they will be nourished by the Creator. At the end of this time, the righteous will not be calling for the mountains to fall on them like the wicked will, rather, they will be rejoicing as Yeshua the Messiah returns to rescue them. Are you training your ears now to hear his voice? John faithfully records the words of Yeshua:

And if anyone hears my words and does not believe, I do not judge him; for I did not come to judge the world but to save [sozo] the world. John 12:47

The Greek word σώζω [sozo] means to heal, save, or rescue. It is the same word that Peter used to cry out for Yeshua to rescue him as he was about to sink beneath the waves, as recorded in Matthew 14:30.

The wicked will be given every opportunity to repent and turn away from their selfishness and violence. They will be given every opportunity to choose to follow the laws of love and peace that govern the natural and supernatural. The earth will shake violently and thick ash from massive volcanic eruptions will block out the celestial luminaries. Eventually the mountains and islands will collapse into the sea. In these tremendous geologic warnings the wicked will destroy themselves.

Friends, the return of Yeshua after the final 3.5 years is most certainly a rescue mission. In His mercy, the Creator of the universe has waited until the very last moment possible to send the Messiah. The Creator's timing is absolutely precise. At the precise moment when all life becomes completely unsustainable, as even the atmosphere is stripped away, Yeshua returns with power, in the company of all the angels of heaven, to rescue his followers.

**HalleluYah to our Creator,
the Most Merciful, the Especially Merciful,
for such a rescue!**

Imagine...
Chapter 18

Slowly awakening, you realize that was the first deep sleep that you have had since leaving Jerusalem. The rocky ground you had been walking over the last three days has finally begun to give way to softer, desert sand. The softness of the wind-sifted sand, combined with levels of adrenaline returning to normal, has finally allowed some rest. The coolness of the early spring breeze coming from off the desert to the south-east strikes your face as you open your eyes and realize it is not quite dawn. You pull the thin blanket closer around, thankful for it as you see that in the cool pre-dawn glow, many of the others in the small remnant of survivors do not even have that much.

The morning star is the only one visible in the east. Even though you cannot make out faces yet, you smile, knowing that a few meters away is your new friend, Zahir, a Moroccan who has already pledged to take a young lady, Rachel from Be'er Sheva, under his wings. They have no blanket, but because of their shared love of Yeshua the Messiah and his ways, they can find warmth together. The conflicting, overwhelming emotions in your heart are pierced by this small ray of hope.

The ground is shaking once again, although not so violently, this time trembling like an Aspen leaf would as the wind crosses the mountain passes back in Colorado. Feeling it, you also feel the grit in the corner of your eyes as your other senses also awaken. The smell of sulphur assaults your nose as you estimate that the journey south has brought the remnant just east of the ancient site of Sodom.

The roar of the volcanic eruptions along the rift to the west has receded into the background noise in your mind, except for when there is a mighty crescendo of renewed explosions such as are now beginning again. Thankfully, the remnant had been able to get out of the vicinity before large chunks of cooled lava had begun falling from the sky, some as large as houses. Turning, you see that the western sky is dark; darker than it should be under its thick blanket of ash. In addition to the grit in the air, there is also the feel of unusual humidity. The tremendous scale of the eruptions has altered the local weather patterns so that it must be raining there.

Although the sound of the thunder cannot be heard over the violence of so many eruptions, the lightning is still visible, even from this distance. It is the only light low on the western horizon, accenting the rising columns of burning ash and rocky debris exploding upwards into the sky from the dozens of volcanos just over the horizon. They are a line of defense, separating you from the horrors on their other side. Staring at this awesome display of power, you cannot help but wonder if the Hebrews fleeing Egypt experienced a similarly confusing mix of awe and hope as they listened to the Creator speak at Sinai amidst a similar display. Where is the Creator now, where is His mercy amidst this catastrophe?

After the mighty deliverance experienced, that is now a so much easier question to answer than it would have been a week ago. A week ago almost all hope had seemed lost. It is hard for you to mark when everything had begun to spiral into chaos as there had always been the usual wars, economic troubles, and pestilences. It was a tough time to be alive as food and fuel were rationed, many had nothing, and violent riots ensued. Even though that was only a few years ago, the memory of that time had already been replaced by more severe trials.

The attack that everyone now just called "the deadly wound" marked a major turning point as humanity had been plunged into a demonic frenzy of hatred and violence. The entire world had gone off to war and genocide; the response to the wound beyond any imagining. Over two billion people killed in a very short time. Countless more died every day from the worldwide famine and pestilences that inevitably followed. Those who had survived knew many prophecies had been fulfilled since then and they were so glaringly obvious, that no one debated about their interpretation anymore; they had lived their fulfilling.

Then there were the asteroids: two initially, and then a third; besides all the other small impacts too many to count. Humanity panicked on hearing of their trajectory and those who were not at the frontlines killed their neighbors just for a pack of bottled water. Surprisingly, the one that impacted the sea seemed to have caused the most damage. Many coastal cities, bastions of evil bordering every ocean and sea around the planet, were wiped out—flattened and erased—by the resulting tsunami as if they had never been there. Navies around the world were decimated; providing a short respite in the war. The spiritual awakening caused by seeing these fiery portents of judgement coming on a collision course with earth was fleeting. Humanity had quickly resumed their violent endeavors, killing even their own refugees fleeing the coasts.

The final war continued, reaching new heights of unspeakable atrocity. Everyone knew exactly who the "*King of the North*" was now. The identity of the deceiver, the beast of Revelation, was obvious; and still the majority followed that religious and political system's sadistic crusade. There were a few who saw the evil on all sides and pleaded with humanity to follow Yeshua's way of peace. Many of those had been killed, but a few, like this remnant, escaped. Many had found their way to Judea. At one point it had been a very dangerous place to be, but then it seemed that, as if for a time, it was in the eye of the hurricane while the storm raged around.

In fact, it was only as the coalition armies conquered the last opposing nation of Egypt that a righteous remnant began to coalesce in Jerusalem. Followers of Yeshua from all over the world, from differing cultures and religions, came together in one place and with unity. And then the reports came, just a week ago, that this great army was coming to invade Jerusalem. The Creator, in His mercy, had brought together this remnant and would surely find a way of escape—and He had done just that.

Your mind drifts back to recall the depths of despair experienced as you had fled, leaving the hills north-east of Jerusalem only to discover the way of escape had entirely flooded. Where the

Jordan River had once slowly meandered there was now a shallow, rising sea covering the valley floor. There had been some rumors that the excess heat being experienced was because the earth's orbit was now closer to the sun. To confirm, several in your group had been noting the days since the last equinox. This new sea also seemed to confirm those rumors. Much of the polar ice would have had melt in order for the Mediterranean Sea to be flooding inland so far. How else could the sea have risen enough to inundate this valley?

Adding to the despair had been the sound of tanks moving on their tracks; echoing off the walls in the canyon just exited. The cry of the remnant had been heart-rending; their prayers ascending in desperate supplication. And then, softly at first, the earth had begun to shake. It seemed that wherever you had migrated the past couple of years there had been earthquakes as they were increasing around the world. Everyone knew what they felt like, but this one had just kept building in intensity. Giant boulders loosened and tumbled rapidly down the hillsides with a mighty rumble. The sound was overwhelming.

It is still difficult to fully describing the unusual patterns to the waves on the surface of the sea that covered the path to deliverance. Finally it became obvious that the sea was being sucked downwards to the north and south of where you all stood. The water drained into these basins exposing a strip of land all the way across the valley. A final shudder, or maybe the overwhelming presence of the Creator had forced everyone to their knees.

And then the shaking stopped, the last rock cascaded to the canyon floor behind, hitting the previous rockfall piled at the bottom with a final, resounding crack. All was silent but for the merest of moments before the spontaneous shouts of joy and praise erupted from the remnant. The sea had just split! The sounds of nature replaced by the sounds of the remnant shouting "*HalleluYah!*" Over and over again. The Creator who had sustained through the trials of the previous tribulation had not forgotten and had just made a path for escape! Running down those last hills everyone appeared to be soaring on eagle's wings. The Jordan River was dry when it was crossed there, just east of Jericho, just as it had been for Joshua, Elijah, and Elisha.

As the remnant began to climb out of the valley, someone had looked back to see the first tank making its way out of the canyons on the other side, followed in rapid succession by many more. In great hordes, they had begun to fan out across the valley, all racing toward the remnant, bent on annihilation. Rather than prayers of desperation however, this time there had been the sounds of expectant victory. As the shouts of praise and faith in the mighty power of the Creator had increased to a thunderous roar, the earth had begun to tremble again. Where just before it had held back the sea, now it crumbled and subsided. The sea once again overtopped that natural dam and rushed down upon all the tanks in the valley below. Across the rising, frothy sea, the few tanks still on the hills on the other side were swallowed up as giant rifts formed in the earth.

That was when the first eruption had violently exploded molten rock up out of the earth. Although across the sea, it felt close—too close. And so the rejoicing remnant had begun to walk. Over the last three days, many more volcanos were created where once there had been none. But they were now distant, between the remnant and Jerusalem was this line of fire and an ever widening sea. Whatever remained of the wicked armies, now in full control of the city, would not be capable of pursuing you and your new friends for quite some time.

A hand touches your arm. Turning back to face the desert you realize that Zahir and Rachel are standing there. It takes a moment for your eyes to adjust from the darkness you had been staring into. The sun is just coming up, filling the space in the sky between the ash laden clouds and the horizon with light. It is overwhelmingly bright. The desert sand is not the reddish color you remember going to sleep on, but is now a brilliant shining white. Startled, you gasp, suddenly realizing that the smell of sulphur is gone; it has been replaced by the sweet aroma of spiced honey.

...

It is now summer, just over three years since that morning when Zahir and Rachel pointed out all the manna to you and you have never gone hungry since. There has also been plenty of rain. So much so, that the wilderness where the remnant has been wandering has turned green. Also, it turns out, that something did indeed happen to the earth's orbit as the length of the year and the months changed.

There is an air of expectancy in the camp today. Everyone has kept the count and knows it has been exactly 1260 days and 42 months since the day everyone calls "the rendezvous". It is called that because there were many more Muslim followers of Yeshua who joined the remnant of Christians and Jews who fled Judea. Those who had witnessed the geologic miracle of the crossing that day have joined together. Since that day, divisions among the sons of Abraham have been fully healed and everyone has become a family.

Everyone knows the end is not quite yet, they have been spending the time studying the scriptures together and becoming a community united in love. There is still another 75 days until the longest of the time prophecies ends: the 1335 spoken of by Daniel. Everyone is hoping that will be the greatest day yet.

The outside world has become unspeakably worse. Reports come in on the shortwave radio of ever increasingly severe earthquakes and eruptions. These warning signs the wicked are ignoring and the violence, famines, and pestilences continue. For the most part, the eruptions have been a blessing in keeping the wicked away and the ash has provided some shade from the increasing heat of the sun.

No one is expecting these last few weeks to be easy. Many have had visions that the wicked have recovered enough strength to once again hunt the remnant down and are intent on wiping them out entirely. However, everyone witnessed the awesome deliverance on the day of the crossing. Everyone knows that the unprecedented wonder that day, in all of its unrestrained power, was a great mercy sent by the Creator for their deliverance; and yet the coming events will be even more catastrophic. The earth will be rendered uninhabitable not too many days from now. But there is no question, for on that final day the Creator is sending Yeshua the Messiah to return and rescue them.

The Author

Ryan currently resides in Sussex, England, where he teaches science, studies the scriptures and writes. His wife, Sherelle, works as a chef, their daughter is attending university, and their son is still being classically educated at home.

He is available to travel and speak to your group whether church, synagogue, or mosque; high school to university. He works independently of any political or religious organization for the sole purpose of bringing glory to the only Creator and reminding humanity of His mercy.

To inquire about speaking engagements, order additional copies of this book or to find additional material such as explanatory figures, read additional articles, and subscribe to the author's newsletter and social media, please visit:

www.RemnantRendezvous.org